# FEEL THE LOVE
# 111 TIPS

## Volume 1

## When Visiting Someone in Hospital

by

Lady Wise

FEEL THE LOVE

111 Tips

Volume 1

When Visiting Someone in Hospital



A catalogue record for this book is available from the British Library.

ISBN 978-0-9933513-2-7

eBook ISBN is 978-0-9933513-0-3



The content of this book is intended to inform, entertain and provoke your thinking. This is not intended as medical advice. That is your choice. It is your life and health in your hands. The intent of the author is only to offer information of a general nature to help you in your quest for emotional and spiritual well-being. Neither the author nor the publisher can be held responsible or liable for any loss or claim arising from the use or the misuse of the content of this book.

Published by Lady Wise

Typesetting by Raspberry Creative Type

Printed by Bell and Bain

# INTRODUCTION

Hi,

A very warm welcome to you for taking the time to join me as I share with you my "Feel The Love" Volume 1 tips book for an improved healing experience. This is the first in a series of "Feel the Love" books to inspire.

The writing of this particular book came about after I experienced 8 months of visiting and caring for my elderly mother, when she took unwell early one morning and found herself rushed to hospital. Up until this time I had had virtually no experience of a hospital environment and the extent to which it can feel a very alien and frightening place for both patients and visitors alike.

Throughout this time both of us went through highs and lows, physically, emotionally, mentally and spiritually. I found it difficult sometimes to know what to do for the best for my Mum while she was an in-patient in hospital. I wanted to make sure that she had all that she needed during the time when I was NOT visiting as much as when I was there for her during visiting times.

When you have a friend, a close family member, relative or colleague in hospital, the first thing you notice as a visitor is how it "changes" your world and your daily routine. This, alone, may become very stressful as each of us seeks to juggle life's challenges.

I thought that if I could list the suggestions that I found helped me to make her stay easier and more comfortable in this seemingly "clinical" environment, then these "tips" could be passed on to you and others like you, to help make your experience less traumatic, less stressful and even more positive than mine.

I hope that this information will make your hospital care-giving and care-sharing experiences as enjoyable as they can be and give you more confidence to work through similar challenges. Humour is a great tonic and healer.

This guide can be read in sequence or at random and includes a sense of humour and often a lighthearted, quirky approach to what could otherwise be taken too seriously!

The suggestions have been broken down into eleven chapters under the following categories for ease of communication in case there is a particular area about which you need immediate help and guidance:

1. Arrival
2. Confidence
3. Hygiene
4. Beauty Care
5. Personal Styling
6. Food & Drink
7. Entertainment
8. Patient Progress
9. Exercise
10. Miscellany
11. Going Home

I hope you are inspired and helped by these suggestions. They are by no means a definitive list. I have worked out that my mother spent on average 250 days in hospitals in her final months and so if I can reach at least 250 individuals and help them with their hospital experience to make it less stressful and a happier life experience, that would be marvellous – one person and their family for each day that my mother was in hospital! Let's make the act of visiting loved-ones and friends in hospital the new superpower for improving the healing experience of these vulnerable individuals.

When you think of suggestions of your own and/or different ways of dealing with some aspects that I have mentioned, I would be delighted if you would take the time to write them down and email them to me at lady.wise@icloud.com

Remember that these suggestions can apply to all loved-ones in hospital including, for example, those who are expectant mothers. Indeed, many of these tips are also relevant to individuals and their carers in the community and those of you looking after relatives, particularly elderly parents, at home too. As this is such a wide subject, I have chosen to focus on the "at home" care for my Volume 2 book which is entitled Feel The Love 111 Tips "When Caring For Someone At Home".

Thanks in advance for all your help.

Wishing you all good things!

Lady Wise

@LadyWiseWorld

# DEDICATION

To my dearest Mum,

Who was the most adoring, loving, patient, amusing and wise lady that I have ever known, ever giving with her time for me especially as a child when I was growing up and always an inspiration and non-judgmental sounding board for many of my ideas and creativity along life's sentimental journey. In her eighty-sixth year of youth, she still continued to make me laugh on a daily basis and loved me, in her words, "more than you'll ever know", until her peaceful passing.

All love, hugs, cuddles and xxx's Mutti

My best friend forever, *Lady Wise*.

# ACKNOWLEDGEMENTS

Thank you to:

My friends who have been there for me throughout the ups and downs of this exciting journey and their patience specifically over the last few years while writing the draft manuscript.

Giuliana DePandi who inspired me to write my own book after she commented in a television interview that she had stayed up all night to write a practical guide to the modern world of dating etiquette. May I just say that it took a little longer Giuliana than I expected!

Clarence B. Jones who inspired me when we met at Aye Write!, Glasgow's Book Festival in 2011. He was kind enough to sign his latest book for me writing, "Good luck with your first book. Dare to Dream."

Marie-Claire who motivated me when we first met at a two day retreat in Glasgow back in 2012. I enjoyed an engaging chat with Marie-Claire exchanging a few laughs and she kindly signed her book for me writing, "Go for your dream!"

Calderfox for providing the beautiful and eye-catching 'heArtwork' front cover and for the image courtesy of Cliparts.com.

# CONTENTS

# CHAPTER 1

## Arrival

This first chapter covers the key points to consider upon first admission to hospital. In many cases this is the first experience for both a patient and their loved one of being in a hospital. When the admission is unexpected and unplanned on account of an accident or a sudden incident, then the stress of the situation is heightened and all the more terrifying. The next four sections of tips focus on ways to reduce the stress over this new situation. This new reality may be an admission to hospital lasting a few hours, days, weeks or months.

# TIP #1 A HAND TO HOLD

## ...it takes two!

The decision to go into hospital may not be straightforward and the holding of a hand can give the necessary encouragement to persuade a potential patient to realise that it is for their own good that they are admitted to hospital – even when they are afraid and feeling very vulnerable.

Often a patient once admitted to hospital can remain in A&E (Accident and Emergency) for several hours before a bed is made available for transfer to the appropriate receiving ward. At this stage the patient is generally in a stabilised condition, but may, if conscious, be a little disorientated with their impromptu and abrupt arrival in hospital, faced with surroundings that are alien to them. Where possible, it can be very comforting for the patient to have their hand held, even if no words are spoken, just to let them feel the love.

Indeed, even as a very close relative, for example, in my case, as a daughter to my mother, who was the patient, the scenario of being in hospital can leave even the best "talkers" to be short for words!

Holding someone's hand should be like a "healing" moment for both parties! Feel alive, feel the love!

# TIP #2 SMILE

## ...even when you are aching!

Most people appreciate an open smile. Such smiles exude happiness, kindness, compassion and at the very least, a split-second love for humanity.

Do not get me wrong, I have come across some really miserable individuals who choose not to smile back even when they are in perfect health!

I am not suggesting that smiles should be restricted to times of hospital admission, but they do most definitely help to reassure the patient at this time as they are often coming to terms with the shock of being admitted to hospital.

The benefit of a smile flows both to the giver and to the receiver. Indeed, often indirectly anybody that catches the smile being given will also benefit. Smiles are recognised the world over, exceeding language barriers and may be the starter required to forge new friendships. The warmth of feeling inside when one receives a smile can truly light up one's heart. For that moment in time, the receiver of the smile can be made to feel special and instantly have their mind diverted away from their own daily challenges. Moreover, even if the receiver of the smile, as the patient, is in some or considerable pain, they can inwardly smile back in an almost knee-jerk reaction to the smile they have received, and it can make them feel a little better.

Be careful, though, that your smile is always a genuine smile.

Fake and half-hearted smiles are nearly always recognised by the recipient and can do more harm to your own reputation and credibility in the long run.

If you do not feel the desire to give a heart-felt smile, you would be better not to bother!

As a patient in hospital there may be some comfort in smiling across to other patients on your ward. My mother was, on one occasion, in a ward of six ladies, two of whom did not have English as their first language. As the days can seem very long when one is sitting in a chair beside the bed and conversation is not forthcoming, a smile may be just enough to do the trick and set "tongues wagging" for the right reasons!

Take it from me... smiling is good for your health.

Laughter lines that show in one's face in older age cannot be bought – nor, in my personal opinion, should they be "botoxed"! These have formed and developed from many shared experiences of joy and fun for which recounting such experiences can be most amusing in itself.

# TIP #3 THE NAMES TO KNOW

## ...names have never been so important!

Throughout each of our lifetimes, there are occasions when the use of a name becomes especially important.

Particular attention is often given to the selection of a name, and may involve hours of thought and consideration. So much emotion surrounds the selection of names perhaps because they generally do involve a voluntary choice, either by a parent or an individual. Not only can they sometimes be traced to naming patterns or used as nicknames, but they can provide valuable hints as to your family history and genealogy. The same names can often be seen used over and over again in families and of course, many cultures believe in honouring their elders and do so by naming children after them. Sometimes the repetition of names can also occur because of an extreme fondness of a particular name. My own middle name, for example, was given to me by my parents in honour of my grandmother on my father's side.

When in hospital it is customary for each patient to have their name noted on a sign above the bed in which they are being treated. It is "best practice" for all staff – nursing and administrative – to have their names on show. I have always found it helpful to make a mental note of individual staff names on the ward and to use these when meeting with or passing by various staff members. The time and effort taken to call an individual by their name can boost the attention of the staff member when you have an issue to discuss with them. Not only does it put the staff member on "alert", but it lets them know that you are taking notice of your surroundings and "who's who". Should you then choose at a later date to either praise the staff or raise a complaint, you do not have difficulty in recalling the appropriate person(s) concerned.

Watch carefully when you next come face-to-face with a hostess or staff nurse and mention their name. Their whole body reacts positively to the emotion of using their name and it appears that they immediately take more of an interest in what you have to say. Therefore, choose your words carefully and use this heightened state of "alertness" to your advantage to convey your message.

In one sad case, a friend of mine was given a "named nurse" for her father who was an in-patient. Each time she visited him, however, she never saw this "named nurse". Indeed, it was only after her father had died in hospital that she met this nurse whose regular work routine was the night-shift!

As patients do not always have visitors to see them at each visiting time, then think about simply saying hello to them when you next pass their bed on the way to visit your own friend, relative, or work colleague. Glance up at their name plate and use their name either at the front of or end of your greeting to them. Once again watch their body language and their eyes; most of them will give a little jolt as if you have just put a "spring into their step". Just as effective as a smile!

# TIP #4 ARE YOU LONESOME?

## ...no-one should be alone

It came as a major shock to me, throughout visiting my mother at least twice every day, how lonely some patients must feel at times, as on many occasions I repeatedly called in on Mum to tell her my latest news to keep her updated and connected to the world outside hospital and often never saw a visitor at many of the other patients' bedsides even for a five minute visit!

Now I can appreciate that at times and indeed, for the occasional individual, the patient may have no desire to have a visitor – family member or otherwise. Back in the 1960's, for example, there was a case presented that considered noise, lack of privacy, and increased stimulation, along with visiting family members, were thought to be exhausting to the patient, although this claim lacked evidence. Apparently, another more recent survey sample undertaken in America consisted of more than one hundred patients. From this, all patients except one wanted visitors. That patient actually requested no visitors and suggested no one else should have visitors as it was disruptive! There is just no pleasing all the people all of the time!

Certainly when my mother was in hospital for less serious ailments, the maximum twice daily visiting times enabled me to adopt a routine, although my mother always found it difficult to say "cheerio" to me at the end of visiting and often wanted me to stay longer as she was less stressed when she knew I was around as a more able pair of hands to meet any of her personal needs. Similarly, when I was present with her we would seldom talk of "hospital related issues" and always talk happy thoughts and stories as a diversion from the clinical environment in which she temporarily found herself at that time.

Latterly, however, when my mother was readmitted to hospital after experiencing the most major type of stroke one can have, a more open approach to visiting hours for me to visit my mother was very important as we had such a strong bond of love for one another. To be in each other's company at such a critical time was very healing for both of us, even although I had been told that my mother, on this occasion, would not, according to the medical specialist, make a recovery. To those of you who have already thought ahead to the increased likelihood and prevalence of environmental bacterial contamination from the open visitation policy, I can assure you that I continued to wash my hands rigorously upon each entrance and exit made to the ward and also upon each entrance and exit from her side room, regardless of whether I was leaving the ward in between these visitations!

Some reasons for the resistance to changes to visitation policies might be because hospital staff and especially nurses may think changes would interfere with patient care or staff shift change. A further reason may be that it may lead to increased stress both for the patient and for the respective hospital staff.

Let us not forget that sometimes ward staff and doctors consider that families may exhaust themselves if they feel they constantly have to stay by the bedside and that restricted visiting hours might allow visitors to rest and recuperate. Nevertheless, the reality is that most of these assumptions are based on opinion and not evidence. It is important, however, that each of us in a visitor role remembers to look after our own health!

Personally, I was fortunate to have the time available and took great comfort from just being in the presence of my mother in hospital in the few weeks prior to her peaceful death.

Recent literature on visitation in critical care suggests that although there are multiple articles on the perspectives of hospital staff and family, that there is a gap in specific literature on the perspectives of the patient. Apparently, there have been few studies related to patient needs and their preferences pertaining to visiting hours. This may in part be because often a patient in critical care can be confused, or unable to speak for themselves, as happened to my own mother.

Interestingly enough, in many countries, there has been a trend towards family-centred care, where the family and the patient are viewed as a unit to be cared for as one during a crisis. The presence of family has been found to be beneficial during a time of need. Families can indeed have a calming effect on the patient as well as provide support and comfort. They aid patients in understanding difficult medical information and have been found to promote cardiac stability, for example. In addition, the family can be the liaison between the medical personnel and the patient, asking questions and improving overall communication. I found this liaison role to be very important when my mother was in hospital. Although I made it clear to all the medical staff that I had no medical knowledge, I was able to translate what was happening to my mother in layman's terms. As I was telling her the situation she instantly felt reassured and calmer about her time in hospital, because it was being retold by a familiar face and voice. It allowed her to voice her fears when I was present and to have those fears allayed in a moment, rather than becoming more confused and worrying about the situation.

The physiological benefits of family visitation have in some literature been shown to decrease the heart rate, decrease stress, and provide no significant increases in blood pressure or oxygen saturation levels. It is of no surprise to me that similar literature has found that nurses at the bedside actually seemed to increase patient stress, yet when family visited, there were no significant changes in blood pressure and heart rate from pre-visit to post-visit.

Unlimited visiting hours can make it more convenient for family members to visit when they are able and also allow the family to take breaks and regroup. Less restrictive hours can give the family a sense of control over the crisis. In my opinion, nurses should plan visitation based on each patient. Each individual is different, and his/her need for family and friends may be variable. A schedule that fits everyone's needs including the ward staff will promote communication and enhance outcomes. Thankfully the care team looking after my mother after her acute stroke acted with the utmost professionalism. They recognised her individuality as a human-being and gave my mother the dignity and respect that she deserved. Visitation hours granted allowed us to be together often. And so, let's just remember to save a smile and a wave for those patients with no visitors at their bedside. Perhaps this simple action could help another patient to fell less isolated and boost both their physical and mental health!

Once the dust has settled on one's admission to hospital it is important to address the confidence of the in-patient. Even for a pregnant mother expectant with her first child, the hospital environment can be a little intimidating. For first time in-patients especially and those individuals who are a little more mature in years, the next chapter on Confidence has a few suggestions to improve that feel good factor regardless of the duration of one's stay and the reason for being admitted to hospital.

# CHAPTER 2

## Confidence

How many of us seek an extra confidence booster, even when in full health? Remember, you deserve to be here! In order to start feeling the joy back in one's life both for the visitor and patient, it is a fundamental need that each person feels a strong sense of self-worth and confidence. The impact of how others see us can directly relate to how well we will feel in ourselves. Imagine when an individual is unwell, often unfamiliar with the hospital environment and unsure of how long they will be in hospital and the treatment they will be required to endure. This chapter shares some suggestions for developing one's confidence and making an in-patient feel more at ease in order to enhance their healing process. Help your loved one to "feel the love of HOME in hospital"!

# TIP #5 ONE TOUCH MAKES ALL THE DIFFERENCE

## ...so reach out!

Very often patients seek reassurance from the strangest of sources. When a loved one or friend is not around, they can be immensely reassured from having a complete stranger listen to them for a few minutes.

A stranger can offer an independent, objective take on a situation and be void of any emotional connection with the patient. This allows them to nod and comment, "Uh, huh! Yes, I know" when listening to the patient speaking and perhaps contributing to the conversation occasionally with, "I'm sure everything will work out for you" and / or "All is well!", an often used expression that my own reiki teacher would say to me on many occasions. Those few words with a comforting hand on my shoulder or a slight touch of the hand on my forearm were reassuring, and at the time seemed to make everything feel suddenly all ok. Remember, we are here on this planet to live our best life!

# TIP #6 WHO IS PRETENDING TO SLEEP?

## ...peek a boo!

Hospital environments can be very distressing and most unnerving for many patients. My mother was very frightened at being in a ward of six patients as she knew no-one else – neither staff nor patients. Prior to going into hospital on this occasion she had been happily in her own home for fifteen months without venturing far beyond the back door and garden. In fact, she had only ever lived her married life since 1959 in the same home!

Although my mother was one to wake up early and stay up throughout the day (without sneaking an afternoon siesta as she did not believe in them) until about eleven o'clock at night, two other ladies in her ward chose to snuggle down firmly under the bed covers. It was only as I gave a passing glance throughout visiting time with Mum, that I noticed their eye-lids flicker and an eye or two quickly shut tight. In actual fact, every word of the conversation between my mother and me was being listened to with full ears and closed eyes!

Now, had either or both of these delicate souls chosen to reveal their consciousness to us, perhaps we could all have had an exceptionally interesting discussion about new buys for the home, the definition of beauty or the meaning of life, for example, but sadly it was not to be.

If, however, one assumes that the other shut eyed patients would choose to listen to your conversation then one can turn this into a golden opportunity for all to share.

I recently listened to the Dutch musician André Rieu conduct an open air concert in Vienna. The backdrop buildings had obviously been carefully selected and the audience was completely engaged by the charismatic talent of André and his orchestra when they were not dancing in the aisles of the open square! I was momentarily disappointed that my mother did not receive Sky HD in the hospital and then thought laterally about how I could facilitate her enjoyment of this evening. The next day I visited HMV and they steered me to André's "Forever Vienna" CD that also included a concert DVD of when he and his colleagues performed at the Royal Albert Hall. Three hours later armed with the CD/DVD player under my arm and my purchase safely inside my black handbag, my mother was both visually and audibly entertained for the afternoon together with her two sleepy bed-friends who were compelled to listen to The Blue Danube, like it or not, as the volume was turned up quite high. Even the nursing staff were visiting the room on a more frequent basis and humming along! Who's for playing "musical beds" tomorrow?

# TIP #7 WORDS OF ENCOURAGEMENT

## ...the need for lip service!

For many of us words do not come easy unless we are born orators and ooze confidence. If, like me, you have a mother who always instilled confidence and love into you in everything you did, each task you tackled, each decision to be made and only ever expected you to "do your best", then the self confidence part grows in you and over time, becomes a permanent facet of your personality. If, like me, your ruling house in astrological terms is communication, then this too can come in handy! Although, even I can be shy at times and seek words of encouragement.

Just think then of someone who even when they are feeling healthy, is below average when it comes to radiating confidence. For such a person to be at an all-time low because they are unwell in hospital and out-with their familial surroundings, the thought of feeling confident about their recovery may be a big challenge. In this situation, the thought of ever feeling healthy again and having partial or full mobility may seem a world away. Gentle words at this time, reassuring the patient to take one day at a time, and restoring confidence in them that soon they will be feeling much better can be very comforting and allay fears of doubt and vulnerability.

Walking through the hospital on many occasions to buy Mum a cup of tea or to buy her a magazine, I would pass by other patients that were in hospital in need of greater care and attention due to more serious ailments than my mother's condition. Sometimes a patient needs the reassurance that there are other patients in a worse state than they are, so that no matter how low they are feeling, they are given some encouragement that their pain is not quite as bad as another patient's pain. Such use of words may seem strange to someone reading or hearing this who is perfectly healthy, but the human condition and mind often work under survival conditions in a competitive way that thinks if someone else is in a worst condition than me then I have greater hope of a recovery sooner than them. Whatever works for your relative, friend or associate, pay them lip service to this and make the time to give them the words of encouragement and support that they need at this fragile time in their lives. You never know when you may be on the receiving end and are glad to hear similar words. Trust your own words of wisdom when reassuring others. Before you speak ask yourself does it improve upon the silence and are the words kind and true? Be practical, be guided and know as you go!

# TIP #8 LAUGHTER BREAKS THE ICE

## ...and is healthily infectious!

Laughter is like music, it transcends all cultures and boundaries and when caught in the right mood hearing or seeing someone laughing and enjoying themselves can become very infectious and you find yourself laughing without understanding why... or the need to know why. A genuine fit of the giggles can actually be quite painful if it gets you like a split in the side! You are doubled up and unable to breathe properly and yet it has an after effect of leaving you somehow lighter in spirit and highly amused for hours.

When communication is poor among patients or when the mood throughout the ward is low, then one person making another laugh can be a real tonic and healer for the whole room! Long after the laughter has subsided it can leave a gap open for conversation to begin.

A friend once told me, "laugh as long as you breathe, love as long as you live!"

If self-worth is the foundation of a healthy body and figuratively speaking what I will refer to as your "house of happiness", then what you say and your choice of words would be the walls and laughter and humour would be the glue that holds everything together. You know what you feel when you laugh – joy!

Remember, the power of joy is unlimited!

# TIP #9 COMPLIMENT THE NIGHTDRESS AND PJ'S

## ...an overnight sensation!

Everyone is an individual and perhaps this is recognised at its best when one is required to parade in one's night attire in front of other patients at night time. Dressing for bed is a very private undertaking and so to find oneself in a vulnerable and unwell state and having to show one's nightwear could make your loved-one feel uncomfortable. The alternative to investing in some new night attire, of course, is to wear the versatile and practical over drapes that the various hospitals provide.

These, however, can lead to interesting tie combinations to hide undesirable "bare-all" extremities and often require the wearer to be a partial contortionist in order to make the tie fasteners taught and firm for several hours of wearing, including the art of tying to facilitate toileting, turning over in the bed and when adopting the semi-supine positioning for comfort.

A neat little cardigan or throw around the shoulders can provide that extra privacy for those who are a little more modest of mind and a little extra warmth too. Style at night is never an understatement and as with all genuine comments a little compliment on nightwear provides another boost of confidence to one's appearance and self-esteem.

# TIP #10 BEDSIDE MANNER

## ...arm-in-arm!

Thankfully, up until the last few weeks of my mother's life, she was well enough to be able to sit up in a chair. It was only at night time that she required to be helped into bed. There is a selection of different functional types of beds used in hospitals that is not always evident to the naked eye and layperson. I realised over time that there were regular care beds with good functional design and reliability, but there was also a more advanced specification of hospital bed that was used when there was a need for increased levels of patient support or bariatric care.

Regardless of stylish design it was important to me that my mother's bed offered great comfort. I am a believer in the healing power behind a quality night's rest. Invariably the cure to daytime fatigue can depend upon the deep restorative sleep obtained from lying comfortably on a robust, bed frame with a quality mattress.

The hospital beds all had side rails for protective care and support and also a hand control to operate the bed's height and profiling function. The operation to release the upright position of the side rails was initially a little awkward until I realised the smooth motion that was required. It certainly did not start off as a means for quick and easy access to Mum! I found myself struggling to find the release button for the side rails and for several days prior to learning the mechanism I had struggled to place my hand between the rail bars in order to touch Mum as I was talking to her. Somehow sitting next to her at the bedside with the rails down was less obtrusive and more personal as we shared conversation and exchanged cuddles!

# TIP #11 TEARS FROM FEARS

## ...cry and dried!

Many of us are seldom seen to cry physical tears and certainly not in public. Men seldom consider it is acceptable for other men or them to cry. I think this stems from the notion that crying is a sign of weakness. For some reason it is considered more acceptable for females to shed a tear. When females cry, males can feel very awkward and some want to make a joke out of the situation. Trust me. Do not do this. Take responsibility and attempt to find out why the person is crying. I agree that it can be confusing on how to react when someone we know starts to cry out of the blue and especially when the reason for someone crying is not made obvious.

If they are not forthcoming with a specific reason, then simply remain calm and quiet, offer up a few super absorbent tissues and be prepared to offer to simply hold the person and give them a hug.

When an individual is admitted as an emergency patient to hospital and has not been in a hospital before, the suddenness of new and strange surroundings can be very intimidating and overwhelming. Often all the person needs to allay their fears and restore a sense of normality and confidence is to see a friendly face that they know.

Tears can roll because of hypertension that has built up, now released and because of anxiety about being thrust into a new environment, often without warning, and the fear of feeling vulnerable. Fear of the unknown when there is a critical medical condition diagnosed can also be very distressing and upsetting. Simply holding the hand of your loved-one can be comforting. Allowing them to express how they feel through a shower of tears is a healthy release of pent up energy and an important part of the healing process.

The reality is that we all cry – some of us, however, cry from deep within our souls and never shed a physical tear, while for others the physical release of tears is a natural process. It is important to understand that on occasion the release of serious water works is very health restoring. Personally, I think that pent up tears only linger to manifest as ailments in other more serious ways if the underlying reason is not effectively dealt with at the outset.

One of the things that many of us are unfamiliar with is the letting go of emotions and indeed showing our emotions. Emotions connect us to create new ways of living and to create new ways of loving, which starts with loving yourself! When we let go fear, we open ourselves up to unlimited possibilities and start to allow the body to heal.

# TIP #12 MANIC PANIC

## ...stress gang!

Is your emergency stress body button, "on" or "off" for most of the time? The stress response which kicks in when you experience either real or imagined danger or distress is the body's way of protecting you. This reaction is commonly referred to as a fight or flight response.

I often comment that a little dose of stress is good for me because it can give me an extra boost of energy and enable me to stay focused to finish a key business task such as a presentation, for example. In a true emergency situation, stress can save your life. For example, years ago I was visiting friends in their flat when the flat above caught fire. We all froze in a state of shock at first while the neighbours stood outside looking up at us peering out of the kitchen window and then we found the extra strength, concentration and common sense to vacate the building as quickly and as safely as possible.

Beyond a certain point, however, stress becomes most unhealthy and can cause serious health damage. Stress can affect your mood, your social and family relationships, your productivity at work, your physical and mental health and your general quality of life.

If you have a lot of responsibilities and worries, your emergency stress body button may be switched "on" most of the time. The more your body's stress system is activated, the harder it is to turn it "off".

So what can be done to put the kibosh on unwanted stress?

I have just a few suggestions on how one's stress levels may be reduced when I think about how I control my own levels: talking to other people; accepting the things that I cannot change; laughing with friends; using relaxation techniques such as ten minutes of deep breathing in a quiet space; changing my expectations on a specific outcome; eating a balanced diet and learning when to choose not to react at all to a specific situation, but walk away from it.

My mother would frequently quote the well known prayer to me as follows:

God grant me the serenity to accept the things I cannot change, the courage to change the things that I can and have the wisdom to know the difference.

# TIP #13 LET THEM EAT CAKE!

## ...beauty and the feast!

Birthday celebrations were important to my mother and were always treated as a special event. It was a joyful occasion when Mum celebrated her eighty-fifth birthday, albeit in hospital, and the nursing staff had arranged a surprise birthday cake for her, courtesy of the on-site canteen chef. Everyone on the ward, who was not diabetic, was able to share in a piece of light sponge cake and this event was a diversion to the normal daily routine for the patients and staff.

To those individuals for whom a slice of cake was not recommended, they were still able to join in singing Happy Birthday.

Any hospital environment can feel very clinical at times and impersonal. Plan ahead and put the extra effort in to celebrate each important birthday. Make sure you put a date reminder of any special dates into either your phone contacts or computer diary. For those of you, who would prefer to avoid the temptation of food as a gift, consider taking in a giant helium balloon or a whole bunch! There are even personalised photo balloons and singing musical balloons as an option. The special occasion can be marked with a talking message tag using your own voice. This might be a good idea if you are unable to visit on the person's special day, but you are keen for them to hear your personal message of congratulations.

Alternatively, you may want to choose this option simply to wish the individual a Get Well, Miss You or Good luck for your operation message.

# TIP #14 NEW NEIGHBOURS

## ...human power!

Every moment we breathe our five senses and more are absorbing phenomenal amounts of input data into our minds. Being in hospital may not always be as mundane an existence as one might think. Our sight, sound, taste, touch and smell are always receiving fresh stimuli.

None more so than when one of the other patients either has to be transferred to another hospital or ward, or go home, making room for another new patient to join the ward. Your interest in this new event may be one of anticipation or apathy. The energy anatomy of each person, like their brain, is unique. What holds true for one person may not be so for another. The introduction to and exit from the ward of one person will change the dynamic of that area. The extent of the impact that you notice from this change on you and your senses will depend on how aware you are of your surroundings. Typical examples of when this occurs each day are when the shift pattern of nursing staff changes; when consultants and doctors conduct ward round visits; the appearance of hostesses and cleaners on the ward; the opening of the ward to visitors.

The examples I have selected are all related to the human effect. These are aside from the effects of general noises that one might encounter on a ward from open windows, medical equipment and bed and chair movements.

The consequence of verbal input received by one's brain is completely different from those general noises that one experiences on a ward. Words impact your emotions!

The power of words can at one extreme make you cry and at the other extreme make you laugh. Words are more than mere sounds. The tone of the voice used in the spoken word can convey fear, enthusiasm, anger, authority, concern and a host of other different emotions.

So in whatever capacity you find yourself in a hospital, stop and think about what you want to say and how you want to say it.

If you are in a ward with a new arrival patient, consider welcoming them with a smile or a brief greeting, to help allay any fears they may have and you may find you make a friend for life!

# TIP #15 STEADY READER

## ...hey, magnifico!

Relaxing afternoon or bedtime rituals might include a little light reading. Imagine how much easier this might be with the use of a magnifying glass.

Hands free magnifiers and stands that are sensibly sized so as not to overpower the user and their available space can be easily purchased. There is a great range of reading aids now available compared to the Victorian times, when most people think of the hand-held magnifier glass as the only option. These include page, text and illuminated magnifiers that are reasonably priced. A bookmark magnifier would make an ideal gift.

These useful items can be helpful not only to the visually challenged user but also for those with reading difficulties. Even those with perfect vision may benefit from using one during the winter months when natural light is limited. For the lucky ones among you, you may be treated to a Kindle reader or equivalent to enable you to make light reading of the situation!

# TIP #16 DON'T WORRY!

## ...wheel a Windridge!

My Mum frequently used this expression throughout her lifetime, "Don't worry, wheel a Windridge!"

For those of you who are unsure what a Windridge is, it is a brand name of a pram manufactured in the West Midlands in England.

Excessive worrying can be very destabilising to an individual and if you are worrying then you are spending time that could more productively be focused on the issue about which you are worrying to more positively impact the outcome!

When you are a "worrywart" you lose time that you never get back and people who come into contact with you can be put off speaking to you if you are negatively moaning and groaning about an issue instead of actively taking responsibility to change the situation.

The path of negativity is a downward spiral and worrying is a fundamental contributor to feeling low and depressed. Do not be afraid to ask someone for help if there is a particular issue that is giving you cause for concern. The first step to dissipating your worry is to understand why you are worrying in the first instance. A lack of understanding or a misinterpretation of an explanation may be an issue about which you have worried for days, only to find out from someone else that you had not fully understood the situation at the outset. Change the way that you look at things and very often a different approach with the support of friends and family will help you to put in perspective concerns that you may have.

# TIP #17 HUGS, HUGS AND MORE HUGS

## ...so what are you waiting for!

Hugs are wonderful! Hugs are magic! Sometimes words cannot express how we feel when we receive or give a hug. If we are lucky, we can change expressions of sadness, isolation or desolation to ones of smiling, happier human beings.

In a global environment of social networking, many of us have become disconnected from being human.

Hugs and cuddles can make even the healthiest of people happier, and so imagine the impact on those individuals who are not feeling at their best in hospital. Share a hug with your loved-one and feel the happiness within as a giver of the hug. Watch the eyes of your loved-one after you have hugged them and view the extra sparkle that you have put back into their eyes. And if you have never hugged someone then be daring and extend your boundaries a little. Feel the energy changing around you and in you. Feel the love!

Remember, hugs are free!

# TIP #18 WILLPOWER

## ...you know you can!

Being in hospital can make you feel stripped of your personality and feeling very needy. In such a clinical environment if you are a person who characteristically is quite timid, then these surroundings could very quickly make you feel highly intimidated and afraid.

It is important for a person to retain as much independence as possible and to be constantly reassured about their state of health. Making someone feel wanted and deserving of the time that you spend with them is an important psychological hurdle to assist in the whole healing process. A person who feels loved will often have a stronger desire to restore their good health at a faster pace than someone who is ignored and left without a visitor.

I think it is everybody's deep desire to feel loved. No-one can quantify the immeasurable value of a kind word, a smile or a reassuring touch, especially when they are feeling low in spirit.

Words of encouragement to someone in hospital that focus on how they feel and how you can help them feel better about themselves form the basic steps of getting them "back to their old self again". Ask them how they like their hair parted, does their skin need a little boost of moisturising cream, are their dentures needing freshened up, do they have enough toiletries with them such as toothpaste and deodorant, would they like some perfume or aftershave brought in, do they have a favourite nightdress or set of pyjamas they would like to wear? Do they have a preferred flavour of fruit drink they would like to have a supply of? All these questions are personal to the individual and their physical and mental state at a particular point in time. In showing them the care you have for them by asking similar questions, you are sending signals to let them know how much they are loved. Someone who is loved has a stronger will to improve their health because they are given possibilities about a future.

On a national radio station, I heard recently reported that there are thousands of individuals in care homes in England who are never visited. No doubt, the numbers are just as prevalent pro-rata when this is applied to the rest of the United Kingdom. For as much as many of us like to consider we are self sufficient and individuals, we are all connected at some deeper level. Each of us is someone's daughter, son, and neighbour; even if that means that the nearest neighbour is twenty miles away. Don't compare yourself to others. You have no idea what their journey is all about. All I can ask is that you take a few minutes to think how you would feel in a similar scenario. If you do not have time to visit someone, send them a card. If you claim to be poor at writing messages then ask a friend to help you write the card, but just do it. We spend too little time finding solutions to every challenge that we are faced with instead of adopting a "can-do" approach. Stop over-analysing with your logical mind and react from your heart! My mother always instilled in me from a toddler that there were no such words as "can't" or "cannot". We would laugh about this when I was older, but the reality is that I choose to eliminate negative influences from my world. You can choose this too, if you want to!

It is what you are going to intend first that will allow you to heal and stand again in a place of joy and peace in your heart. Presently the greatest power on Earth and in the Universe is the human power of intent. When you intend to have LOVE enter your life the healing can start. LOVE is the power beyond all power. It is profound! It is INTENT that will open the door to your "house of happiness".

# TIP #19 JUST A NOTE TO SAY

## ...a bit of all write!

Writing effectively is still important despite the modern day impact from computers, tablets, iPads, texts and emails rather than choosing to write a handwritten letter. When you are simply determined to make some notes for yourself to make sure that you do not forget or miss out any questions you may have, then your writing style and ability are not so important.

Be sure to keep a little notepad and pencil or pen handy in case you find that you or your loved-one has had a visit from a doctor or nurse and has not fully understood what was being explained. Instead of feeling anxious or nervous about the issues mentioned, take a little time to write down a few notes. When your family member or friend next comes in to visit you, you can tell them what has happened and if they cannot understand your interpretation of events then they can find someone present who can allay your fears and help you.

One of my friends recently had the misfortune to break her ankle and needed immediate surgery. Afterwards when she was required to attend a physiotherapist for treatment, she found herself coming out of the appointment without having asked several questions she had planned to ask on her way in! The conversation and exercise routine had simply taken over her thoughts of what she wanted to say. In this instance, had she written down her questions before going into the appointment she could have ensured that all her questions were answered before she came away from the treatment room and she would have excused herself the need to worry about anything.

If you do not feel comfortable writing down words, then make up your own symbols and abbreviations so that you know what they mean. You can then translate these for the individuals that will help you later.

Both my mother and I have been in consultations with a doctor and have thought that we were assimilating all that was being said. I remember nodding my head in acceptance of the information supplied. Once I left the hospital I could not remember the conversation. I had unknowingly been so emotional about the events going on that I had only temporarily absorbed the doctor's comments. It is always best to take a few notes to refer to at a later date and then there is no frustration built up over forgetting points made. This can be especially relevant when exercises and/or medication is necessary. If your loved-one forgets the exercise routine they may be in danger of overexercising and delaying the healing process!

In this chapter I have provided a few tips to improve one's confidence at such a stressful and vulnerable time. The most basic need of an in-patient, that I regularly hear from friends, relatives and former patients themselves, however, is to know that there are high standards of hygiene to minimise the risk of picking up an infection while in hospital. Hospitals do seek to maintain high standards of cleanliness but from my experience it does no harm for an extra pair of eyes to observe that your loved-one or friend is recovering in the cleanest possible environment and so Chapter 3 focuses on tips concerning hygiene.

# CHAPTER 3

## Hygiene

Keeping both the environment around you and your body clean is vital in combating illness and also in preventing future health challenges. Improvements in personal hygiene will improve your friend or loved one's healing experience. Let's now take a look at fourteen hygiene tips.

# TIP #20 JUST A COMB THROUGH THE HAIR

## ...are you making headway!

We can all do with confidence boosters along life's journey. The health issue for which a patient has been admitted to hospital will affect whether a daily shower or bath can be given as part of good hygiene. The frequency with which a patient's hair is washed may also be less than they would ideally like, on account of health reasons, mobility issues and/ or the time available for staff on the ward to devote to your loved-one personally. There are various ways around this wash routine that can make a positive difference to how your loved-one feels and looks. Ensure that the patient has a good comb... with all teeth present, straight and clean!

Be sure to choose a comb or a brush designed for your loved-one's hair length, thickness, and texture. A bad quality comb or brush may damage one's hair! A comb or a brush is something that should be used for the hair everyday!

Steps to get ahead!

- use the comb to untangle, style, or to "comb out";
- be very gentle with the use of your comb;
- take your time when you use your comb and consider it a part of a relaxing grooming exercise;
- always start combing from the bottom of your hair and work your way up as you undo any knotted or tangled hairs;
- a comb will not slide through tangles, and so gently work out the tangle, as this is ultimately better for your hair.

Hair combs are among the oldest tools known to mankind. It is considered that they have given countless users an advantage over the centuries from a variety of parasites that would otherwise have plagued them.

## SELECTING A COMB

*Metal hair combs*

The most popular of these metal combs are those bought for ease of slipping into a pocket or handbag and are approximately 12cm or 5 inches in length. They are very durable and go from narrow to wide teeth.

*Wooden hair combs*

Good quality wooden combs are usually handmade and polished. They can be made of boxwood, cherry wood or other pine wood. The choice of comb is personal, in my opinion, I would favour a wide-toothed wooden comb in place of a hairbrush or a fine-toothed plastic comb. Why? Well, wooden hair combs are anti-static and have no sharp seams, and are unlikely to snap or tangle hair, especially when the hair is of mid to long length. I tend to think of mid length and longer hair as hair that is at least just touching one's shoulder.

My own personal favourite comb is from Switzerland from finely crafted hardwood and measures about 12 cm or 5 inches long. One of the reasons I particularly enjoy using this comb is that it is easy to slip into my handbag, the teeth are strong and not too close together and it combs my long hair without static. The action of combing can provide a massage to the scalp that is very soothing. I find it gets even better with use!

*Plastic hair combs*

Plastic combs will keep your hair healthy and tangle-free and are often inexpensive which is good for the purse!

*How to clean hair combs*

Now that you have made a purchase of a new comb, here are some guidelines on how to clean your comb that should take no more than ten minutes;

- remove all hair from the comb;
- prepare a warm water and liquid soap bath;
- dip the comb several times into the warm soapy water;
- rinse the comb with cool water;
- let the comb air dry.

Just a comb through the hair can make someone feel appreciated and cared for. Perhaps the suggestion of a different hair parting than normal could even be the catalyst for a positive change that makes your loved-one feel really good about themselves. The act of combing someone's hair can be a very relaxing motion and is a basic primal habit that even relaxes gorillas – or so I am told! Remember that we often refer to the expression that if our hair looks good we feel good! In this case feeling good as part of the healing process leaves no excuse from attending to our loved-one's hair. For those of us with loved ones who have experienced some hair loss and who have perhaps lost some confidence because of this issue, I would suggest you choose to refocus on an area which is a stronger feature such as nails or beautiful eyes to make them feel good.

# TIP #21 SOFT SOAP?

## ...go on flatter yourself!

Using a beautiful bar of handmade soap can really make you feel refreshed and while making and using hand-made soap can be a rewarding experience and a natural way to keep your family clean, few of us has either the time or the inclination to go to these lengths.

So how can we keep good personal hygiene and still feel good about ourselves in hospital? What is a hospital antibacterial soap? These soaps have chemical agents in them that can kill off bacteria and so hospital grade antibacterial soaps are very important in controlling the spread of bacteria in hospitals and reduce the risk of getting infection. That is all very well, but I am talking about bathing and the use of soap beyond effective hand washing.

In order to protect the patient from getting and spreading infection, I suggest bringing in their own favourite bar of soap for a specific use – say a weekly bath. Place the sealed fresh bar of soap in the patient's toilet bag and either leave a handwritten note inside or at the first opportunity tell one of the nurses what you have done and explain that this is for specific one-off use for the patient, as you are aware of the tight hygiene standards. In this way, your loved one can enjoy a small "home-comfort" to lift their spirits and make them feel extra fresh. The hospital's provisions that are made available can tend to be very different to the patient's usual choices. Using items such as soap that you are familiar with and trust to look after your skin can give great comfort.

# TIP #22 A FLANNEL FOR "FANDS"

## ...cleanliness is next to godliness!

Doctors Wendell-Holmes and Semmelweis proved back in the 1840's that infection and disease were being spread by the unwashed hands of medical colleagues and simply washing hands well between patient visits reduced the risks of cross infection dramatically. Unfortunately as with most pioneers, the majority of the population doubted them and it was not until Louis Pasteur came along that more attention was paid to the impact of having clean hands at all times.

I believe that poorly washed hands are as much a touch-contamination risk as unwashed hands, yet here we are at the turn of the twenty first century and touch-transferred infections still present a major health problem throughout the world.

As a young child, my mother and her young brother would call their hands, "fands" for fun and probably also because her young brother at that time was still learning how to pronounce the "h" sound! As a child, my mother was apparently always obsessed with keeping herself clean and as part of her daily wash would use a flannel or face cloth to which it is often referred. She would really enjoy taking a bar of soap in one hand and holding her flannel in the other, she would wet the flannel and then lather it up with the soap and enjoy the feel of it on her "fands and face". This was just another way of exfoliating and allowing the old cells to be discarded.

Nowadays, there are face cloths that are designed for one-time use, although these are more expensive as a result, and they also differ from the traditional flannel in that they are specifically designed to wash your face.

If you do choose to take a flannel in to a friend or relative, remember to ask them to use it only once and while you are there so that you can bring it home with you and boil wash it, before bringing it back another time. This will avoid any disappointment of losing it, as happened several times to my Mum, and therefore save you money!

In one of the earlier hospitals in which my mother was admitted, a face cloth was stipulated on the list of things to bring in. When she was moved to the next hospital, I was never given a list of what was required and I never thought to ask! As a result, I ended up losing three new face cloths, because in this particular hospital they were not allowed and without asking, the nurses on the ward just threw them out!

# TIP #23 TOOTHPASTE RUNS OUT

## ...no toothpaste kisses!

Many patients have been admitted under emergency circumstances and the last thought that they have when they have left home is to pack a toothbrush or other related toiletries. Remember to look around the hospital when you next visit and find out if that particular hospital has a donations programme for accepting toiletries. Some hospitals have arrangements to accept the donation of brand new items such as toothbrushes, face cloths, soaps and toiletry bags for patients. This gives them a chance to freshen up and feel more human again!

I would recommend a non-fluoride toothpaste and if you are really stuck an alternative to toothpaste would be to use some bicarbonate of soda mixed with a little lemon juice.

Why is it that always before that special date, outing or even job interview, a spot appears unannounced in a prominent part of your face!

Well you can now relax because...as an aside, allegedly, a simple application of toothpaste can eliminate spots really quickly! Although there are various creams etc. that claim to remove spots, depending on which toothpaste you use, this easy way to get rid of spots may be cheaper and save you a special trip to the pharmacist or supermarket!

# TIP #24 THE ADVENTURES OF DENTURES

## ...gum-ho, gung-ho!

If, like my mother, the patient wears dentures the chances are that for a variety of reasons the cleaning of these may be overlooked while the patient is in hospital:

- the patient may be too embarrassed to ask for help with their dental hygiene;
- they may have been rushed to hospital without packing denture cleaning materials;
- they may feel a bit low and cannot be bothered with the exercise.

For whatever reason, these dentures will need cleaning. It may not be something that a friend of family relative may think about if they don't use them themselves or know of anyone else who does. This is unfortunate because it really is important and can affect mood, ability to eat and drink and can be very uncomfortable if neglected. Again it may be worthwhile taking the patient's usual cleaning materials into the hospital.

I can remember my mother frequently enjoying a round of raspberry jam, bread and butter in the summertime, but then bemoaning the fact that she had to give her dentures and mouth an extra thorough clean and wash out to ensure that no stray raspberry seeds were trapped lurking underneath the gums! If neglected, these could result in a very painful and uncomfortable experience that in some cases could later give rise to a mouth ulcer. Yuugh!

Looking after your own hygiene needs can lift your mood and ease the process of eating and drinking. Although if you are ever with someone who is feeling a little nauseous and you know that they are wearing dentures, can I recommend that you ask them to take them out before they rush off to the bathroom. This can avoid an expensive trip to the dentist! On one occasion when Mum was still living at home, all of a sudden one evening she felt a little sick. I helped her through to the bathroom just in time for her to put her head down the toilet! In order to get rid of the vomit quickly I speedily flushed the toilet only to find that when my mother raised her head, you guessed it, she only had one upper set of dentures. Her lower set were now long gone on their travels through our plumbing system with zero chance of recovery! Fortunately, for Mum she did have a spare set and so I just changed her over to these, but she was most annoyed and it was too late for me to do anything except to say, "sorry!"

Despite dentures being held in place by their natural suction to one's gums, and I know that sometimes a fixative may also be used, in the case of someone tilting over their head to vomit there is going to be every chance that any good suction will be lost. I believe that dentures can be fixed securely in place by dental implants or mini implants now, which can give you the confidence to eat whatever you want without having to worry about your dentures coming loose or falling out!. Lucky you!

# TIP #25 BRUSHES HOLD BACTERIUM

## ...brush strokes in warm water!

As a child I liked nothing better at night than for Mum to brush my hair. When in hospital such simple tasks can seem like a pipe dream away and are not always given time to happen. So next time you visit someone give a thought to whether they would like their hair brushed and at the very least make this a parting shot!

Dirty hair brushes can be the perfect playground for attracting bacterium. Why would you want to brush stroke more dirt through your locks after having just washed your hair? You wash your hair and so why not your hair brushes! Apart from the hair that you brush out of your head, your hair brush will attract various oils, dry skin flakes, grease, dirt and bacterium.

A hospital environment is no excuse for not washing your friend's hairbrush.

So firstly, wet the brush with warm water and make sure that the bristles are pointing downwards. This will prevent water going up into the handle. You may or may not be able to use a sink that has a plug.

For hospital sinks with a plug, you will then be able to dispense some anti-bacterial soap on to your hand and shake this into the water. Take the brush and then shoogle the bristles gently in the warm, soapy water. You can use your fingers to make sure the grease and grime is removed from every brush follicle. Rinse the brush with warm water until the water runs clear. Now you can pat the brush dry against a paper towel or hand towel if you have brought one in to remove any excess water.

For hospital sinks without a plug, you will then be able to dispense some anti-bacterial soap into your hand and shake the bristles across your palm to ensure every bristle gets a coating of soap. Holding the brush firmly, run warm tap water and shoogle the bristles gently underneath the running water across the palm of your hand. You can use your fingers to make sure the grease and grime is removed from every brush follicle. Rinse the brush under the warm water until the water runs clear. Now you can pat the brush dry against a paper towel or hand towel if you have brought one in to remove any excess water.

# TIP #26 PILL SPOTTING

## ...thrills and spills!

Under Tip #29 I write generally of love spills, but I felt it important to focus specifically on pill spills too!

A couple of times when I was visiting my mother, my eye would observe a small tablet on the floor either near to where Mum was sitting or under the bed. My first reaction was to be worried about the pills that I saw on the floor for several reasons:

How would I know if the tablet was part of Mum's medication or simply one that had fallen from the pharmacist's cabinet on his/ her ward round?

Was there a chance that my mother had missed taking one of her pills? Would this affect her overall medical condition? Was this a one-off occurrence? If I did not say anything about noticing it, who would and when?

As a general suggestion, the safest bet is to ensure that no children are likely to pick it up off the floor and pick the tablet up yourself; then take it to one of the medical staff on the ward and ask them to dispose of it. To avoid needless worry, it makes sense to do this without making a fuss and alarming the patients nearest to the pill spill. The medical staff should be told of exactly where it was found in order to determine to whom it belongs!

Avoid trying to be a Pill Identification Wizard and let the medical staff match the size, shape and colour to their prescription database!

Similarly, I would arrive for visiting and occasionally find that my mother's tablets were still lying in a little pill pot. While the pharmacist had performed his/ her obligation to dispense the necessary medication, there was no check to observe that my mother was indeed going to take her medication.

Sometimes patients can experience difficulty in swallowing pills and the fear of choking on them can put them off taking them. The nurses are aware of this problem and will often ask the patient if they would like the tablet broken up for them.

The wonders of medicine now provide for both pill crushers and pill splitters!

The pill crusher is a handy device that enables pills to be placed in a small container and ground down to a powder, while the pill splitter can assist with dividing up the pill and/or tablet, making it easy to use thanks to a high quality stainless steel blade. It is a small, neat device that can fit into a pocket.

For any of you that hold medicines at home, it is also a reminder to periodically check your medicine cabinets for any expired, re-bottled, or unidentified pills. To avoid mistakes and unwarranted confusion, I would ensure all medications are kept in their original bottles or packets, with pertinent labelling and instructions attached.

# TIP #27 BED, NO BUTTER!

## ...removing all the bed crumbs!

When someone is in hospital for even two days, there is the chance that they may have accidentally dropped some crumbs from their breakfast or morning drink into the bed.

Nursing staff are generally vigilant but with the current restricted resources, they do not have the same time to check every "nook and cranny". Small particles of bread, toast, biscuits, cake and sweets can easily get caught between the sheets, culminating in a very uncomfortable feeling for a patient. One afternoon as I was lifting some magazines off the bed covers, I found a small stray dod of butter!

# TIP #28 UNDERNEATH THE ARCHES

## ...clean as a whistle!

One of the common proverbs which my mother used frequently and which has been proffered as dating back to the Hebrew writings was, "Cleanliness is next to godliness".

While my mother was keen to know that she had a clean bill of health from her doctor, I was concerned whether the environment in which she was temporarily living would meet with my own approval! Surface contamination can be difficult to eradicate due to the ability of microbes to survive on wet and dry surfaces for extended periods.

Without wanting to cast aspersions and put the cat among the pigeons, whenever I visited Mum, one of the twice daily tasks I would do was to scour the floors, her chair and bedside cabinet in her ward for "little bits". These bits were pieces of unwanted matter that had accumulated around my mother throughout the course of her day. Very often these could range from medical tablets to tuna meat from the salad served at lunch. I would even find empty plastic jam dishes under her chair, when I arrived for afternoon visiting that were from her breakfast that day! My more immediate concern was to whom did the tablet that was still lying on the floor belong and hence, who had not had their full medicine quota that day? It is said that a little knowledge is a dangerous thing, but the little that I do know is that some tablets are prescribed to counter the side effects of others prescribed. If there is no check to ensure that all of a patient's medicine is taken, then surely the optimum benefit of the concoction is not allowed to work?

Allegedly, the Department of Health estimates that with good practice and careful hygiene, around 15% to 30% of all health care associated infections could be avoided, saving thousands of lives and the NHS an estimated £1 billion a year. Moreover, a hospital's failure to meet its infection control obligations can result in numerous penalties including improvement notices, adverse publicity and in more serious cases, prosecution.

One would therefore expect that every hospital staff member would take responsibility for ensuring a continuously clean, healthy environment both for their patients and for themselves and fellow staff members. I do not make a habit of leaving litter around my own house and when infection control is such a key issue in a hospital environment, this does not meet with my idea of high standards as acceptable by the NHS National Institute for Health and Clinical Excellence...not NICE!

From my experience I think we all as visitors to hospitals have a duty to be more vigilant about keeping the environment clean and preventing health infections and that extends beyond the regular use of anti-bacterial spray for clean hands! Who is that I hear calling out, "Bring back matron!".

# TIP #29 LOVE SPILLS

## ...have the wipes handy!

While is very important to try and maintain one's independence when in hospital, there are inevitably moments when one has little accidents. I term these "love spills! There is no use in losing one's temper or spouting forth belittling remarks like, "Oh for goodness sake, can you not watch what you are doing?!", because we all have such moments. Although it is the most natural thing to want to speak out, this is one of those occasions when it is more diplomatic and polite to simply keep calm, shut up and clean up! Remember, hospitals are unfamiliar environments to the majority of their patients and these surroundings may exacerbate an element of hypertension without the need for you to spoil the visit (precious connection time) by showing up your friend or relative's inadequacies at one of their most vulnerable times in their life.

Love spills can be disguised in many forms: sometimes these involve the spilling of juice, water or maybe even a leaked catheter! Paper towels are not always made available on the ward without having to ask for them. One way to avoid any embarrassing delay is simply to keep a small packet of tissues or handy moist wipes in your handbag or pocket. There is even a variety from which to choose, varying from those that are anti-bacterial to alcohol free and biodegradable, fragranced to fragrance-free, and for children, there are also wipes that can be purchased to remove felt pens, crayons and water based paints.

If you are unsure about the hygiene of clearing up a love spill then simply press the buzzer to alert a member of ward staff of the issue and ask for their help.

# TIP #30 BAG IT UP!

## ...lose one's bottle!

Keeping the ward tidy must be difficult for the ward staff. Interestingly, each patient has their own levels of personal "stuff" either brought in by themselves on admission to hospital or slowly drip-fed to them by their visitors. I have no idea whether the amount of clutter collected in and on a bed-side cabinet in hospital is in direct proportion to the propensity to compulsively hoard at home, but it would be an interesting case study!

I, however, am keenly advocating that less is more. There is no point in holding on to items that are worthless, hazardous and especially unsanitary.

Feng Shui specialists will tell you that if one's space is energetically clear as well as visibly looking clear, then mobility, physical and mental well-being all have a better chance of improvement.

And so next time you visit your friend, family member, relative in hospital look around for any empty bottles, paper wrappers and used tissues that they have now finished with and either place them in one of the many waste bins that are kept in each ward, or put the rubbish in a bag and take it out of the hospital with you!

# TIP #31 ALL CHANGE

## ...clothing casualty!

It can be so embarrassing to find that a trip to the toilet is made too late! Those kegel muscles need to be exercised! It is estimated that some 6 million people in Britain suffer from some form of incontinence. Medication, ageing and childbirth all have their role to play in the deterioration of the pelvic floor muscles.

The most common reasons for incontinence in an ageing patient, in my experience, occur when a patient becomes anxious and the anxiety brings on a bout of stress incontinence; they have not pressed their buzzer in time to ask to be assisted to the toilet or they have had to wait on a commode that was already in use on the ward. Certainly on three occasions when I was present, my mother pressed her buzzer for assistance and had to wait eight minutes each time for a commode to become available!

There are also other kinds of incontinence: urge incontinence, bladder control problems, night time enuresis or bed-wetting. There is, however, a remarkably huge range of disposable products to suit all incontinence needs and there are many washable incontinence products offering protection from incontinence with the benefit of being reusable rather than throw away to meet longer term needs and to assist individuals when they return home and no longer have the same care offered to them.

As a general rule, therefore, it is helpful to ensure that an extra change of clothing is made available for the in-patient. This provides for a quick and easy change and avoids further embarrassment of the individual having to be made to wear a hospital gown in place of their own clothes that is not so comfortable or stylish!

No-one should be left to be uncomfortable, wet and smelly! Instead make sure they are always in a position to be "in the very pink of the mode!"

# TIP #32 SINK RINSE

## ...pull out all the stops!

Each of the wards would generally be equipped with a minimum of one municipal sink. As this would be available to all the medical and patient staff, good hygiene was essential.

Once Mum and I had enjoyed our cup of tea I would rinse the cups out in the sink. Every evening I would clean Mum's dentures in the sink and so it was critical to ensure the sink was left clean for the next user.

While I was never in a predicament that caused the sink to be blocked, I did make sure that all stray hairs and tea leaves were fully drained away!

# TIP #33 ALL THE LAUNDRY

## ...the great unwashed!

Whatever your home habits, I like to have clean nightwear and day clothes on every day. This can be quite a demanding goal to meet when you have someone staying in hospital, especially when their medical condition can affect their situation and put added pressure on clothing needs.

There are patient clothing bags provided and these are boldly labelled and usually discretely on display in a ward for you to see when you visit. I would suggest that you carefully check to ensure that all your loved-one's clothing is there and that you have not picked up another patient's clothing by mistake. My mother almost lost two nightdresses and one dressing gown because a patient in the bed next to her had a penchant for clothes that did not belong to her! On one afternoon when her son came visiting and went into her bedside cabinet to pull out his own mother's dirty washing, he pulled out two of my mother's nightdresses! He was in complete shock when I excused myself and told him. Fortunately of all the coincidences, I had attended the same university as him and so I vaguely knew him. He was rather mortified, but these things happen. After that incident I stitched and indelibly ink marked my mother's name into all her clothing appropriately.

Remember if you are tasked with the laundry cycle to separate whites from coloured clothing, don't let those stray black socks slip into the machine with your white shirts by mistake.

If you are in a rush and you have cotton nightwear to wash, then you will probably be able to skip ironing these provided you hang up the garments carefully to dry and avoid being crushed.

One of the challenges that I had with Mum, initially, was to turn around her nightwear quickly enough to keep her in fresh nightdresses each day. I was able to buy a few new ones over the period that she was in hospital to ease the strain on the essential wash cycle. In winter and times of poor weather, the call to meet the clean clothes deadline can be a little problematic. Give yourself plenty of time to plan for when and how you will do the necessary washing.

When you have any marks on items, do your best to identify what they are first. A good catch all remedy is to use a little washing up liquid and gently rub over the stained area. Rinse with cold water and if the stain persists then apply a little more washing up liquid before putting it into the normal machine wash cycle. A couple of aspirins will freshen up the colour of the clothes, particularly white garments. Be careful to put only a little washing up liquid on the affected garment to avoid loads of bubbles frothing up your machine!

For garments that have been ironed and require to be folded for carriage to the hospital, ensure these are hung up as quickly as possible on arrival to the ward so that your efforts receive full appreciation.

In conclusion of this chapter on personal hygiene I have listed tips that suggest good hygiene will help your friend and loved-one not only to look more attractive, stay clean and encourage them to recover from their ailments quicker than they otherwise would, but to feel more confident and healthy which may lead to improved interpersonal relationships with everyone with whom they come into contact. Chapter 4 looks at taking the basics of personal hygiene one step further and looks at beauty tips for maximum feel good factor!

# CHAPTER 4

## Beauty Care

Beauty for me is all about how the inner beauty of the soul is nurtured to shine through our whole being. This inner happiness if you like, is what is perceived as outer radiance or beauty to others. In the same way that each of us has a favourite piece of music, favourite book or film, or favourite car etc., beauty is unique and specific to each individual. For example, I have a favourite painting that depicts an old, windowless, rusty VW car which has been abandoned in a dense country forest. It is autumn, however, and with the sunlight breaking through the thinning trees capturing the hues of the autumn leaves that have fallen around the car, this 'old wreck' that would to anyone else be described as junk, looks beautiful to me. Feelings of inner happiness will complement the recovery and healing process. It is NOT about what others think! I believe it is important that each individual explores how beautiful they feel to themselves, not to anyone else or to please anyone else. In this chapter I have suggested a few tips the result of which may encourage your loved-one or friend to feel happier and a more beautiful, peaceful person in a way that will stay with them once they have been discharged from hospital too.

# TIP #34 LIPPY DOES THE TRICK

## ...looking ten years younger!

Now I know that not everyone likes to wear make-up. Sometimes I think that for those who choose not to wear make-up they have an inverted snobbery about beauty that has them persuaded that make-up is "dirty" or is "simply a mask" to the real person. Personally I have worn lipstick since I was fourteen and would take great pleasure in watching my mother unpluck the lipstick cover from its elegant holder, twist it up and holding the hand-mirror in her left hand, carefully start drawing the scarlet red lipstick from the top of the upper lip to the left and then repeat the gliding motion from the centre of the upper lip to the right. Opening the mouth a little wider, she would then tilt her head up about 15 degrees, draw her mouth up and back and then bring the right hand in to the bottom left hand corner of the lower lip and pull the lippy firmly down and round the protracted curve and release gently back to base! A little touch-up again on the upper lip and she was ready for blotting. For those of you who consider that the act of blotting merely defaces the lippy just painted on and furthermore dilutes approximately 40% of the colour in a wasteful manner, I would point out at this stage, that in order to prevent the subsequent audit trail left across various tea and coffee cups, not to mention the artificially inflamed rosy cheeks from the trace of kissing, this latter procedure is recommended.

A further tip that I would share with you is to apply a light base coat on your lips of foundation. This will persuade any lipstick to stay on just a little longer!

So anyway, after application of lippy there is an immediate transformation. My mother's whole face seemed more radiant and she genuinely looked at least ten years younger. This tiny task was an instant health boost to my Mum that also added a touch of glamour to the ward and won numerous positive comments from the passing nursing staff, visitors and fellow patients. This is clearly a very inexpensive confidence booster at a time when one can feel very low and have low self-esteem and confidence. How amazing then to feel as if one has waved a magic wand to make everything better if only for a few moments with a mere small tube of lippy! The brightening of the lips is a make-up enhancer that is not only used in makeup applications today but also featured heavily in Egyptian times.

For those of you who find your lips are a little sore or even dry, perhaps an undercoat of Vaseline or a suitable moisturiser would suffice before applying a little lipstick colour.

# TIP #35 MOISTURISE THOSE HANDS

## ...skin tight, skin bright!

It is very seldom that I take time out to think about the torture to which I subject my hands every day – dirt, pollution, opportunities for getting scratched, catching a nail and just generally knocking them as a result of performing everyday tasks around the home and office. In the same way that a car needs to be washed regularly, polished and occasionally wax protected to preserve its body, so too do we owe this treatment to our bodies and especially our hands. By using just a little cream on your hands you can condition, sooth and moisturise them to leave them feeling incredibly soft. Your hands deserve the same level of care as your face.

If you have not yet experienced a paraffin wax treatment, these are generally available in spas, beauty salons and good nail bars. The wax is warm and soothing and your hands will be left feeling soft and supple.

While I would recommend a paraffin wax hand treatment at least every six months to lock in moisture, this is not available and practical in a hospital environment.

The next best thing, however, is for one of your friends, relatives, or visitors to bring a little jar of moisturising cream with them and to dip their clean finger into the cream and dab the cream on to your hands, wrists and forearms, if possible, and gently massage it into the skin. For those of you who are feeling especially generous with your time, you could offer to give a little hand massage too! The cuticles around the nails are always quick to dry out and the higher temperatures that are maintained in hospitals mean that skin can become dull and dried out quicker than perhaps at home.

If this simple treatment can be applied on a daily basis then it will plump moisture into the hands and leave them looking younger and provide firmer looking skin. A moisturising lotion or cream not only hydrates your skin, but also improves elasticity and helps to protect it from all the elements. Beautiful skin can be attained no matter the age of the person.

Men have dry hands too! Most of the time men tough it out because the fragrance of hand cream can seem too girlie and is too highly scented! If skin gets too dry, then it can become itchy and that can cause discomfort and frustration, so bear this in mind when you are visiting and choose a fragrance free option when possible. A non oily hand cream will still nourish and protect, but heal your skin without the embarrassment of greasy palms!

It should not be forgotten that the main benefit of this skin care treatment is to lavish attention on your loved-one and to make them feel needed, loved, cherished and relaxed.

# TIP #36 FACIAL PAMPERS PLEASE

## ...remember the neck and décolleté!

Sometimes the hospital environment can seem very boring and tiresome. There is, in my opinion, no place like home and yet in order to have the required care, time must be patiently spent away from home. If you feel tired, then it is probable that you may look tired. The skin's appearance can be instantly improved with a little exfoliation and moisture too!

It's so very important to exfoliate your skin. Skin cells are shed at an amazing rate every minute of every day. If you don't get rid of them, they will remain on your skin making you look dull and dry. No matter how much lotion or moisturiser you use, you are never going to have glowing skin if you do not exfoliate. Cleansing is arguably the most important part of your basic skincare routine. Proper cleansing gets rid of old surface skin cells, dirt and dust, grime, make-up and bacteria, and keeps skin pores free of clogs and able to breathe freely.

Gently rub your facial exfoliator in circular movements on your entire face and neck and rinse clean. This circular action aids circulation and acts as a preparation for the skin to receive topically applied nutrients and moisturiser. Continue to do this 2-3 times a week for year-round beautiful skin. If a facial exfoliator product is not available to you then I would use a cotton wool ball and some glycerin and rosewater. Rosewater is a classic English beauty tonic for the skin and the glycerin provides moisture to the skin. I find that the combination of these two acts as a marvellous cleanser for the face.

GUIDELINES TO PROPER FACIAL CLEANSING:

I suggest cleansing twice a day, regardless of skin type. Some of you may have heard that if you are to cleanse your skin this often it will strip it of precious natural oils. I would say that if you do not cleanse regularly, and especially before you go to bed, then there may be a build up of toxins in your skin which may make the skin prone to a break out or rash.

Choose a cleanser that is appropriate for the skin type. I prefer not to use soap simply because it can be very harsh and drying. Equally, a cleanser that is too rich can cause the clogging of pores while too dry a cleanser may irritate the skin. Dry skin cleansers will generally contain oils and various herbs to improve the dry condition, whereas herbs that balance oil production and support clear skin will mainly be found in a cleanser for oily skin. If the skin is particularly sensitive then a fragrance free cleanser is recommended. Personally I still use a natural cleanser that includes rose water rather than soap and water. My grandmother used glycerin and rosewater and apparently was always receiving compliments on her glowing skin. Here's hoping it continues to work for me!

When water is an option to cleanse the face then make sure it is tepid and not too hot. Hot water tends to damage skin over time. Cold water does not dissolve and take away embedded dirt and so warm water is best.

Always make sure any sponge, facecloth or flannel that is used is clean and made of soft material so that it does not scratch the skin. Of course the alternative to this is to use one's fingertips. When working around the eye area I would suggest using the 'ring finger' to take away any persistent dirt. Why? Well, for most people this finger is the weakest to control independently of the other fingers and so it works in a more gentle way on the skin's surface without pulling the skin.

Ensure that hands are washed thoroughly before cleansing the face to avoid any dirt being worked into the skin. For those of you with a fringe, longer hair or simply hair that 'does not do what it is told', then I would suggest using a headband to keep hair away from the face.

Firstly, splash lukewarm water on to the face and neck area.

Apply the cleanser with either a soft sponge or your fingertips. Gently massage this across the face, neck and hairline using small circular strokes. This motion will help remove dead skin cells and is not too harsh a method for removing grime from your face. Remember to be extra gentle around your eye area.

Rinse with lots of lukewarm water and ensure that around the neck and hairline is well rinsed of cleanser.

Gently dab off any excess water with a soft towel. A moisturiser appropriate for the skin type can now be applied. When this is applied immediately after having dried off the skin, most surface moisture will then be sealed in. Once the exfoliation treatment has been done, then offer your loved-one a light massage using a dab of moisturiser on your finger and then gently rub it on to the face and around the neckline and décolleté. Soft, gentle circular movements for applying the moisturiser can be extremely soothing and this action often brought a smile to my mother's face when I did this. Please make sure that you have no sharp nails before you start, though.

# TIP #37 A NIGHT IN HONG KONG

## ...perfume power!

Perfume, itself, is thousands of years old and the word "perfume" originates from the Latin "per fume" which translated means "through smoke". The reason I enjoy wearing perfume so much is that the choice of fragrance selected can have such an amazing effect on one's mind and body...instantly! A squirt not only gets the dirt as my mother would say, but can leave you feeling very tranquil and extremely serene. Yet, with just another few drops of differently scented aromatics, you can feel very beautiful and very special.

Whatever your preference from among the many essences and oils, these perfumes can help you seek momentary release from the material world and permit you to escape to a wonderland all of your own.

Many historians consider that the earliest use of perfume bottles dates to around 1000 BC and is Egyptian. The incorporation of perfume into Egyptian culture was a choice equally favoured by the ancient Chinese, Arabians, the Middle East, Greeks and Romans. Phoenician merchants even traded in Chinese camphor.

Now I can remember as a child the defining aroma from the chest oils that my mother made up for me whenever I had a slight cough – she would mix up equal parts of eucalyptus, camphor and mustard oil. It smelled absolutely fantastic and it worked a treat! I would jump into bed and enjoy falling asleep breathing really deeply to inhale the pungent potion and wake up fresh in the morning with a clear chest! It was most unfortunate when the law ceased to allow the sale of some of these oils over the counter. These old remedies really did work!

Hospitals have a penchant for producing their own unguents, however, that do not always leave behind the most pleasant of aromas.

A couple of sprays of your favourite Eau de Parfum can soon have you dreaming of "A night in Hong Kong", rather than the confines of a hospital ward. The fragrance can have you in your dream whisked away to the exotic Orient whose name means "fragrant harbour". It has a wonderful subtropical climate and makes for an ideal stopover with beautiful mountains and rocky islands.

## TYPES OF PERFUMES

*Pure Perfume*

This usually means that between 25 to 40% of the scent is pure aromatic compound. The higher proportion of aromatics will generally indicate a more expensive price and therefore often pure perfume products are very exclusive.

*Eau de Parfum*

This scent is generally made up of between 15 to 30% aromatics. It is usually a combination of scent agents with a diluting mixture. These perfume products generally increase in price based on the amount of essential oils included; this has a direct impact on the amount of scent noticeable on the body, and the length of time it lasts. It is often a much stronger-smelling scent than Eau de Cologne or Eau de Toilette.

*Eau de Cologne*

This scent contains between 5 to 15% aromatic compounds and is made from a mixture of essential fragrance oils. Sometimes Eau de Cologne is considered interchangeable with toilet water.

*Eau de Toilette*

This scent contains between 3 to 5% aromatics. This is a very light scent and is generally applied liberally. The scent tends to fade quite quickly and so you may need to reapply it at least once throughout the day.

*Perfume Oils*

These are similar to perfumes, with the exception that the solvent is oil based rather than alcohol based. If you have dry skin, you will probably prefer this type of perfume rather than other types mentioned where the alcohol content is too drying. Oil-based perfume can be formulated into a solid perfume with the addition of a little melted beeswax to make a waxy block that can be rubbed on the skin.

So let "Ointment and perfume rejoice the heart" Proverbs (27:9)

Where should you apply it for best effect?

- spray a small amount individually on each wrist;
- behind your ears;
- on the backs of your knees and
- lightly across your hair.

Remember that perfume may stain clothes and can have an adverse effect on jewellery (making it dull and discoloured) and so it is best to apply your favourite type of perfume before getting dressed.

Two of my own personal favourite scents are camphor and sandalwood. Camphor was frequently used in early Arabian perfumes and the crystals formed from oil extracted from wood. Sandalwood oil is sourced from the heartwood of a tree and tends to be fragrant and fixative. With a penchant for such strong aromas I wonder, can a choice of a favourite perfume be linked to the strength of one's personality? I am sure there must be someone who has researched this!

Apparently, Hong Kong city life is attractively diverse, so I think your perfume should be too! Seek to cheer up your loved-one in hospital with a little spray of their favourite perfume or aftershave and notice how much better they feel if only for a short while.

# TIP #38 MAKE-UP CONVERSATION

## ...first blush, finishing touch!

You may be a person who does not naturally wear make-up, that is unless like one of my friends, who was recently hit in the face with a hockey stick, by mistake of course, she found herself wearing foundation to cover up two black eyes and stitches on her nose! Equally, you may be someone who feels naked unless you are wearing your make-up even when you are in the house and on your own! Either way, when one is in hospital for any length of time, a little dash of make-up can make all the difference to how you look.

The perception of how you look to other people can affect how they treat you and behave towards you. Remember, that each of us is literally "living in our own world". The perception of how we think we look to other people may not be matched with the reality of how they really see us from their world.

A recent email I received invited me to a business seminar about building your personal brand from the inside out, i.e. projecting oneself to others in business to improve your career. The email mentioned that research tells us that people make very important decisions about YOU within 7 seconds of meeting you. This book is about helping you and your loved-one or friend "Feel the Love" while in hospital, but the research I am sure holds true wherever you are and truthfully, if you feel good about yourself then you will unconsciously exude an inner confidence that others will be attracted to and feel they want to help you all the more. This in turn can help you with the challenges that must be faced when in hospital.

Perhaps all your loved one or friend may want is a little face powder to make them feel good. Perhaps this may be the first time that the suggestion of wearing a little make-up has ever been made to them in a long time, and they merely enjoy the chance to just talk about make-up without actually trying on any. The fact that you are giving of your individual time to talk with them about a different topic to the norm may be the boost in confidence that they need to show a smile! It only takes the use of seventeen muscles to smile and yet the face uses over forty muscles to frown, so why would you want to expend more energy on feeling sad?

If you are visiting someone regularly and over a long hospital stay it is important to constantly be stimulating them with new and interesting topics of conversation. Sometimes in our busy lives, we do not make the time to talk about everyday things and we rush around and then regret not making time to discuss the latest issues. Make this the time to make-up for those lost words and precious moments! Watch the happiness in someone grow as you give them the time to ask their opinion on something and listen to them for their answer!

I digress, and so back to make-up!

The choice of make-up will depend on skin clarity and colour, ranging from pale to light olive to deep brown. In the heat of hospitals I am thinking that just a light touch of micronised mineral makeup might make all the difference to a dull, flagging complexion.

When this fine powder is applied to one's face it gives an effortless and natural look. It is also excellent for effectively covering up any blemishes or skin imperfections without being claggy on the skin. These minerals have the added benefit of concealing large pores and minimising the look of fine lines and wrinkles. For the more health conscious readers, these particles do not penetrate the skin and so there is no threat to harming the bloodstream.

Application suggestions for a flawless finish are to take your powder holding a clean, large brush and lightly touch the brush into the powder and then touch the brush to your cheeks, across your nose and chin and across your forehead.

For a healthier, more radiant look, apply a different brush with a light bronzing powder and simply swirl across your upper cheek bones. Get glowing girls!

# TIP #39 EYE, EYE!

## ...what a spectacle!

Use the opportunity while your friend or loved-one is in hospital to make sure that their eyesight is ok and is not preventing them from enjoying a good read or watching a good film, for example.

If you know that they wear a pair of glasses even for the occasional routine task then check that their glasses are clean and that there is a spectacle case for them to be carried in to protect them for when the owner is not wearing them. Another good suggestion is to ask them if they have a spare pair of glasses available. Even if they choose not to have these on the ward, if they have told you where they are kept at their home, then it could minimise any delay and undue stress should their regular pair of glasses accidentally go missing while they are in hospital. Alternatively, ask them who their optician or optometrist is so they can be telephoned if there is a problem.

When the next opportunity arises for them to have a new set of frames then it might be an idea to suggest something slightly different than they have previously enjoyed simply to give them a small change in their daily routine and to cheer them up. This may be a change in the colour of frame that they opt for and /or the style of frame that is chosen. You'd be amazed at how such a little change can positively impact on how your loved-one is perceived by the world around them.

# TIP #40 FOOTSPAH!

## ...a foot note to follow!

Being in hospital is no excuse not to keep your feet in good condition. Mobility and flexibility can be significantly impaired if a person has foot problems. The more mature person may also wear special socks, pads or footwear to address imbalance and relieve foot pain.

My mother before she went into hospital was a regular wearer of support hosiery and in hospital many patients find themselves wearing compression stockings to allow necessary support and recovery from a variety of leg ailments.

In the same way that we can all feel the benefit from a manicure, so too can we enjoy a pedicure. Even just a delicate massaging of the feet, toe areas and around the ankles can leave the recipient feeling much better.

I used to take in a small jar of moisturising cream and a beautiful crystal glass nail file. When the ward was quiet I would duck under the table and take Mum's shoes off and start to gently file down her toe-nails. The file can also be used to get rid of any hard skin that has accumulated on the outside edge of the foot or heel. I have been using a crystal nail file for about five years, but they have become increasingly popular because they leave each nail feeling so wonderfully smooth and they do not have a tendency to tear a nail like some other nail files. It is a rare product that feels as good to use by the user as the feel good factor benefit to the receiver! These files are made from hand cut toughened crystal glass and are very long lasting. The only reason I had to throw away my first crystal glass nail file was because I had accidentally put a heavy bag down on my hand bag and the angle of the file sitting up in my bag split the file in two. My most recent file is now carefully packed away in its case each time for safety!

The benefits of a giving your feet a little attention are well documented. For those who are keen on reflexology, you will already know that our whole body is essentially mapped out on the soles of our feet. Certified reflexologists have specific treatments that they will offer. The benefits of professional reflexology are often stated as improved energy levels, improved blood circulation, improved immune system and reduced stress.

I am just talking about giving a little gentle stimulation to induce a parasympathetic state of restfulness and relaxation. Massaging either hands or feet will release serotonin. This is a feel good hormone to make an individual feel calmer and give them a relaxed mind state. Make sure your hands are clean and then dab on a blob of moisturising cream and gently massage it into the feet starting at the toes and working down the foot to the heel, almost mirroring the flow of the body from head to toe! You can play your part as a caregiver in the healing process, with minimal effort.

Some of us do not like our feet and so this may be the first occasion that your loved-one has ever received a mini foot massage. This is all the more reason to take your time, feel that you want to give this experience, and then go with the flow! You can then go home and tell friends that you did some work as a "sole soother". It makes a change from watching the television!

I feel very strongly that beauty should be about each individual being different and helping that person to shine in their own skin for who they are. It is not for each of us to fixate on one specific image of what beauty in today's society should be. Each of us is individual and so let's celebrate this individuality by taking it to the next level. In Chapter 5 I look at personal styling tips to appreciate the uniqueness of YOU!

# CHAPTER 5

## Personal Styling

Personal styling often implies that in order to be stylish one has to buy a whole new wardrobe to look good. This is so untrue! I consider personal styling to be about satisfying an individual's need for comfort and how good they feel about themselves. Are you with me on this? There is a theme running here that is focusing less on the materialism of what brand of clothes one wears and at what cost, and focusing more on taking the time to listen, talk, and really care about your friend or loved one's ideas and thoughts of what aspects of styling make them feel good about themselves when they are in hospital and there may be certain practical issues to consider as part of the personal styling process. Yes, it goes back to nurturing that inner feeling of happiness which in this particular chapter can be expanded from the benefit of introducing a few external styling tips!

# TIP #41 AT THE CUTTING EDGE

## ...get ahead!

How many of you enjoy a visit to the hairdresser? A hair cut or simply a wash and blow dry can make a woman feel fabulous!

Take note of a flyer or notice board announcement on entry to the hospital and ward that advertises the services of a mobile hairdresser to the hospital. This is a great way to offer a practical treat to your family member or friend.

There is usually a menu of treats together with a price list and days that the mobile hairdresser will visit. All that I did was to put Mum's name down on the list on the ward notice board and stated that I wanted her hair to be cut and blown dry. As I wanted her hair cut as well, I brought in a photograph of her favourite hair cut and wrote down a few instructions. I left it on top of her bedside cabinet at the side of her bed with an envelope marked for the hairdresser's attention. I put the exact money inside the envelope for the hairdressing service together with a tip as a thank you and a memo note of thanks. The envelope was then sealed and left with the photograph for the next morning's visit. When I arrived to see Mum at visiting that afternoon her hair looked beautiful. She had her lippy on and the stunning cherry red colour choice looked great. I could tell that she felt a million dollars.

This simple act gave Mum a sense of pride in herself again and she also apparently thoroughly enjoyed the talking point about her photograph with the hairdresser, which had been taken for a modelling shoot she had had done at 71 years of age.

# TIP #42 WEARABLE SHAPES

## ...make way for catheters!

Whether a permanent or temporary scenario, there may be various adaptations to be adopted in order to wear comfortable clothes in a hospital environment. Clothes that flatter a person's body shape will make the wearer feel good, but in hospital one has also to think about the ease of washing garments, the extent to which fabric creases, fabric durability, practicality and the choice of a fabric that is naturally comfortable against one's skin.

Frequently, the wearer will be sitting for much of each day and so the selection of a fabric that is fairly crease resilient will be good, such as, a lightweight denim, cotton or polyester. Fabrics that I would tend to stay away from in hospital would be silk and linen, although a blended mix of linen with cotton, for example will crease less than 100% linen fibres.

The use of separates can work well not just to make the wearer feel good about themselves and be aesthetically pleasing to their eye, but also for ease of use when it comes to dressing and toileting. If your loved-one has a small accident over breakfast, lunch or dinner, then a top or shirt is easier to change than a dress if the wearer is in a wheelchair. Think about choosing tops with a short, loose sleeve, for example, as even throughout the winter months the hospital wards remain warm. Mum never once wore a jumper in hospital, although occasionally she wore a stylish cardigan to keep a chill at bay. Tops or fine jumpers with a three-quarter sleeve will prevent cuffs getting dirty. Sleeveless tops and t-shirts on the other hand can be just a little too cool and often not so attractive because the whole of the upper arm is on display. If the upper arm is not toned then a short sleeve looks more flattering to the wearer.

Think about contrasting textures and simple adornments to garments to give them a touch of exclusivity and panache!

Although one way to modernise an outfit of any kind, whether excessively casual or very smart is through the use of accessories – jewellery, belts, and shoes, I would guard against wearing anything expensive in hospital because that may add unnecessary anxiety to the wearer in case the item is lost.

The key is to provide your loved-one with clean, adaptable and adaptive clothing that is attractive and functional yet easy to use. In this way it offers the wearer as' much independence, dignity and comfort as possible, whilst looking good!

I am specifically differentiating here between adaptable clothing and adaptive clothing. When my mother was in hospital I was unaware of the extensive range of adaptive clothing that is mainly sold by specialist outlets serving wheelchair users and those individuals who are physically challenged. I worked purely from my own initiative and the idea of "stepping into my mother's shoes" (which incidentally I could do because we both shared the same shoe size!), to imagine how she would best feel and cope with the clothes she was wearing caused me to consciously choose more adaptable clothing for her to wear. It became obvious to me that the use of elasticated waist trousers would be easier than zips, and that the use of Velcro fasteners would be preferred over buttons.

My mother had always taken an interest in personal styling and with a passion for fashion and personal styling myself; I still wanted Mum to look good in hospital even though she had to start wearing a catheter. Although my mother's natural preference was for a well fitting trouser with a narrow leg, she had reached the stage when this would no longer be an option. Instead, I found some inexpensive plain cotton wider leg trousers that would allow her to wear a catheter reasonably unobtrusively yet remain comfortable and be easier to open for toileting and dressing. It was important to find apparel that was still well fitting and suitable for her figure. The use of a solid coloured fabric on her legs meant that I could focus on dressing up her upper body to detract from the part of her body that she was not so keen on. I also found attractive elasticated waist skirts that were made with a blended lycra mix of fabric for stretch. One idea would be to find a wrap over skirt as an alternative to an elasticated or zip skirt. This design makes it much easier to wear when the wearer has either lost or put on some weight.

In selecting a capsule wardrobe for hospital that still flattered my mother's body shape, she was able to appear confident and stylish. This was most important to the healing process and attracted many favourable comments from other patients and visitors that made her feel good.

I have since become aware, however, of trousers on the market that have a fold-down front allowing ease of access to catheters, for example. These clothing garments are specifically termed adaptive clothing because they are manufactured and tailored for the physically challenged and wheelchair user market. Trouser openings, for example, are often concealed behind what looks like pockets and so the garment still looks fashionable. The drop front is securely fastened with Velcro fastening. When fastened these look just like ordinary trousers, but they can be opened down very easily to improve continence management.

Adaptive clothing is generally specially chosen for its ease of putting on. They cater specifically for those individuals with poor manual dexterity for example and even carers appreciate the ease of dressing using these specialist garments. I think the fact that these garments look good is extremely important to the wearer.

The emphasis up to now has been on items of clothing but my mother also experienced great challenges in finding the right shoes and slippers to wear on her feet. She suffered from oedema which is a condition that causes too much fluid, in her case mainly water, to accumulate in her body. Any tissue or organ can be affected, particularly the hands, feet and around the eyes and sufferers may experience debilitating swelling. My mother suffered oedema in her feet and her ankles and the tops of her feet were particularly swollen. Latterly, this made the wearing of ordinary shoes for her an impossibility. There are several products, however, to help with this condition, because it is very important that feet and heels are protected from resting continuously either on a footrest or in a bed. I found a pair of beautiful fleece slippers that were comfortable and met the needs of my mother's swollen feet. They provided an alternative to an adjustable slipper and wrapped the feet in soft wool.

Although I have mentioned coping with these changes to the capsule wardrobe while in hospital, after a patient has left hospital there may be a need to continue to address these issues. Those suffering from physical limitations caused by strokes, arthritis, paralysis, diabetes, oedema and incontinence, for example, may leave hospital with an ongoing need for wardrobe and dressing care. In order to preserve independence and confidence, a review of one's wardrobe attire may be a practicable solution. For others the prospect of living in a nursing home or having a carer attend to you in your own home will necessitate a simpler way of working too!

I think it is important to mention that I noticed that many companies selling adaptive clothing also cater to meet the challenges of children who are physically challenged, although I have no direct experience of this.

One of the features of adaptive clothing is that there is no reason why some of the garments cannot be used by the general population. Maybe we will see a new young designer challenge mainstream fashion with new adaptive and adaptable styles for show at London Fashion Week next year! Strut your style stuff!

# TIP #43 I LIKE YOUR HANDBAG!

## ...Gucci or Prada?

One of the downsides to being in hospital is often the lack of privacy afforded each patient. This can make it difficult to feel "at home" by surrounding the patient with their own belongings such as a handbag; for fear that it may be stolen from the patient's bedside cabinet.

An alternative to taking one's handbag in to the hospital would be to find a suitable smaller purse for a few coins to be placed in. I would then find a larger toilet bag for a comb or brush, cosmetic purse and other personal items to be shared with the toiletries. In this way, your loved-one does not need to fret about looking after too many bags!

Never one to miss an opportunity for a laugh, even when she was a patient, my mother was as witty as usual on this particular sunny afternoon in hospital.

She was sharing a ward with three other female patients and her bed was positioned by the window, next to the toilet facilities. I had not long arrived to visit her, when the patient across from her stood up and walked across by the window past the two of us to go into the "ladies powder room". Now this particular patient had her own health challenges and required to hold her transparent catheter bag as she walked. Judging from the colourful liquid slushing around in the bag, her physical parts were obviously working well. Without hesitation, however, my mother piped up, "Oh, excuse me. I like your handbag!" The patient looked at her aghast and then burst out into laughter. Both Mum and I then dissolved into hysterics. I had always known since a young child that my mother adored the wonderful accessory called a handbag, but had not realised that such unusual, quirky bags held such appeal! A few days later when the octogenarian was waiting to be discharged from hospital, she called me over during visiting time to say how funny she had found the comment made by my mother to her a few days ago and that this "chance to chuckle" would remain with her, long after her return home.

# TIP #44 CLOSET CONTINENTAL

## ...best bib and tucker!

As a keen traveller to central Europe, I have always admired the casual, relaxed style of dressing on the Continent. It is this non fussy, easy feel but with a touch of originality at an affordable price, that I would like to suggest you seek when wearing clothes in hospital.

Variety can be offered through colour options and colours can be used to brighten not just our wardrobe but also our mood! The Egyptians long ago used colours to impact on and treat physical, emotional and mental problems.

Black, brown and tan are excellent colours for using as a wardrobe staple for the selection of trousers and skirts. These are colours that tend to mask dirt and stains easier than white.

Variety can be encouraged with both colour and design for T-shirts, tops, blouses and fine knitwear as separates to the hospital capsule wardrobe.

Lemon, peach tones, lime, pink, turquoise, green and white all complement these three staple colours, which means that the upper body wear selected will be interchangeable. This key factor is a practical solution when washability, for example, may become more important if there are time constraints on visiting, washing and carrying out one's everyday tasks too!

Strong deep colours of navy, red and green against one's complexion I would tend to keep for wearing once one is out of hospital because when one is unwell, these colours can be very draining against your natural skin colour and make you feel less healthy.

T-shirts that are finished with unusual stitching round the edges can give the appearance of a more expensive and unique look.

Some fine sweaters now have a detachable collar, which provides a dual look – choose to wear with or without the collar attachment for a change.

A piece of clothing can look quite different if it comes made with pockets than without, and then there is a choice of which type of pocket – a welted pocket, a flat pocket, a piped pocket or patch pocket! My mother always liked her trousers and jackets to have pockets so that she could put a handkerchief in them.

Pleated frills, ruffles and ruches are best left at home as they could be irritating when worn in hospital.

In addition to day wear, one has to think of night wear too. There is a choice of pyjamas or nighties and perhaps a little bed-jacket for warmth. My mother found nighties to be the easiest to wear when she was also wearing a catheter. Otherwise one needs to consider the width of the leg on the pyjama trouser for fit and comfort. The fabric and style of the nightie is important too. Nightwear in hospital is best if it is made of cotton or a cotton and polyester mix. This is for durability, practicality and washability. The shape of the neckline should be considered when purchasing nightwear as some individuals do not like to feel "hemmed in" if a facing comes right up around one's neck. There are over thirteen different types of neckline styling, but rather than bore you with these I would advocate one of the following four:

1. a square neckline, this forms half of a square at either the front, the back or both;
2. v-neck is the edges coming together in the shape of a v at the front in the mid-chest area;
3. scoop neckline is a curved front neckline;
4. a sweetheart neckline, which looks like the bottom of a heart is very flattering to most wearers.

I would discourage selecting either day wear or night wear that has a round neck because it fits close to the wearer's neck. Plunging, draped, bateau (neck tapering to a point on the shoulders) or décolletage necklines are all more dramatic choices and can be saved for when one is feeling healthier. Simple necklines minimise the probability of accidental damage through handling, carriage and washing.

# TIP #45 DOLCE BANDANA

## ...keep stray hairs at bay!

Bandana headbands come in a variety of colours and patterns and are usually about 5 to 7 cm or 2 to 2.5 inches wide. If your friend or loved-one has a good head of hair and you choose to give them a mini facial or mini makeover while in hospital, then a bandana or equivalent headband may be useful to avoid stray hairs getting in the way of a stroke of moisturiser or between fingers when massaging their face. My own hair grows slowly enough without losing more unnecessary hairs along the way!

The use of these is also practical if one has any skin, ear or eye irritation or infection. It can help to keep hair away from the infected area without causing added irritation.

Alternatives to the bandana that would be just as practicable and acceptable would be a regular hair band or an Alice band. One of these would not only make a perfect, practical, low cost gift to take into hospital for your loved-one, but it would also add instant style! The choice available is amazing with bands for all occasions including crystal sparkles, bows, flowers, pearl effects, all offered in a massive range of colours. What a great way to lighten one's mood!

Remember that these can be kept clean with a regular dip in soapy water under a warm water tap!

# TIP #46 LINGERIE BRIEFING

## ...bottom line technologies!

Do you like wearing your underwear or is it time for a change?

Underwear is very important to give shapc to and boost confidence for the wearer. There is a wide variety of lingerie available and sometimes this choice can seem a little overwhelming to the individual who simply wants to feel good in what they wear and feel comfortable. Style is very personal but still affects the lingerie choices that we make.

While in hospital, I would suggest that comfort becomes the priority factor. If your loved-one already has everyday underwear that meets their comfort criterion and is stylish that is perfect.

My mother was in need of new underwear soon after she went into hospital and it can be a little tricky buying something so personal for someone else. I have a few guidelines that I hope will assist you when you find yourself in this position.

Underwear styles for females fall mainly across the following categories:

- Maxi or Full Brief: these offer the most coverage across both the bottom and stomach area up to one's waist.
- Midi Brief: these sit about 2.5 to 3 inches (5-7cm) below the tummy button whilst retaining full bottom coverage.
- Maxi/Midi Brief with High Leg: these offer a similar stomach and bottom coverage as previously mentioned but have a higher cut on the legs which is very flattering to most figures.
- Light String or Thong: there is both minimal styling and minimal material to this style which offers a string that sits between one's bottom cheeks at the back with a high cut leg and narrow sides.

Other variations on the above include the hipster brief which has a low rise and sits across the hips, and tanga briefs which are more risky in appearance than the thong, with a high cut style to the back.

My mother was most comfortable wearing the classic styled midi brief with the high leg. This style offered her comfort and support across both her front and back areas, but gave her good movement of her legs by being cut higher than other briefs.

Continual innovation of design and technology now offers a diverse selection of stylish shapewear garments too. To have so much choice can be a little confusing and for everyday hospital use I would recommend leaving all shapewear at home, unless an express desire is made known. Very often, nursing staff do not like to know that the patient is restricted in any way because they may require medical attention that demands a quick response and access to all body parts. Saving the shapewear for a more appropriate occasion will keep it safe and in good condition for your loved-one to look forward to wearing when they are feeling in better health.

The selection of underwear should include consideration of the type of materials used in their manufacture. Traditionally, briefs were made from a high quality fine cotton for excellent comfort. Today there is a much greater choice of fabrics available. Some briefs are made from soft micro fibre for smooth fitting and comfort. This material may be a combination of both polyamide and elastane. Other briefs contain a blend of high quality lycra and fine cotton to ensure a good fit. For everyday wear and washability in hospital I would recommend ideally a blended mix of high fine cotton content with a single digit percentage of lycra or elastane material. This should provide the wearer with a soft stretch fit that is perfect for comfort.

Now we have not yet discussed cups, cradles, wings and slings! Yes, that's right – bras! One of my friends is an expert bra-fitting specialist and apparently as ladies we are not so hot on ensuring our bras are correctly sized. Lack of proper bra support can cause painful symptoms. Equally the wrong fitting bra to the wearer can generate discomfort from straps digging into shoulder areas, underwire bending up or riding up at the back and underwire pinching one's skin.

Is there a quick fix short term solution?

I think not. In addition to correct fitting, which requires the expertise of a professionally trained bra-fitter, a person who has been hospitalised may relate to one or more of the following conditions:

- pregnancy;
- loss of muscle tone and elasticity of the skin;
- loss or gain of weight.

To even think that you could select the perfect, fitting comfort bra for your family member or friend would be naïve. There are so many different bra types including sports bras, full cup, support, front fastening, strapless, mastectomy, plunge and the many others not mentioned. What to do?

Unless the patient owns existing bras in which they feel comfortable, then offer to bring in a little vest or t-shirt in to them for extra warmth, if needed, that they can wear under their day clothes until they are well enough to be expertly fitted for a new bra.

# TIP #47 GOODY TWO SHOES!

## ...have you rebooted?

It is always worth checking that both feet of your loved-one are correctly wearing a pair of shoes or slippers and that these have been correctly placed on the appropriate foot. It sounds common sense does it not, but you know the phrase, common sense is not so common!

I have heard stories from friends who have rushed into work wearing one navy shoe and one black shoe. How embarrassing! Ha!

Slippers and shoes can easily go astray in a hospital, especially when one is unfortunate to have dementia, when forgetfulness can play a part in their disappearance and accidental misplacement.

As with my mother's clothing, I was very careful to mark her slippers with her name on the inside label using indelible ink. I also selected slippers that were machine washable for ease of cleaning. As my mother had oedema, her swollen feet made it very difficult to find a correct fitting shoe.

How can you choose a shoe that properly fits you? Finding footwear that comfortably fits can be a challenge.

If you are asked to bring in shoes for your family member or friend who is in hospital, give a thought to where the patient is likely to be walking whilst wearing the shoes. Will they be going outside? What types of surfaces will they encounter? A shoe that has a slippy sole will not inspire confidence in the wearer, particularly if they are not too steady on their feet. Consider if the shoe provides good support to the wearer around the heel and ankle area. The height of the heel should not be too high. While I enjoy wearing heels, I would suggest a heel of no more than two inches in height is practicable for hospital use. A slight heel will give added arch support to your feet. Think about the weather conditions. If the person is likely to go outside for short periods and it is the winter season, then open toed shoes are not recommended. If it is possible take in a pair of flat shoes and low heeled shoes then the person will have the opportunity to interchange them on their feet. Some individuals can experience back and hip pain if they wear heels for any length of time.

Perhaps as a special treat you could suggest going with them once they get out of hospital to have their feet properly measured for a new pair of shoes!

# TIP #48 COVER A MULTITUDE OF SHINS

## ...put a sock on it!

The oedema on my mother's legs created a swelling of her ankles and feet. As she found putting on tights too stressful and restrictive, there was a great selection of socks available to ensure she was warm and comfortable at all times.

There are specially adaptive socks available too with extra ankle width that will stretch gently to accommodate swollen legs and feet without creating pressure.

The choice is huge and is not restricted to colour, pattern or size. There are cable knit bootie socks, thermal socks for those who have circulation issues and like extra warmth, leg warmers if you feel your legs only need a little heat boost, wool bed socks, sumptuous slipper socks and there are even ones with a safety grip on the sole of each sock.

For those individuals with highly sensitive skin it is perhaps best to restrict any sock purchase to those made from natural fibres like cotton, merino wool, and angora. Although there are beautiful, fluffy mohair socks on the market, anyone with asthma or breathing difficulties may find these too irritating and itchy on the skin, so choose carefully.

# TIP #49 WHERE IS GRANNIE'S CARDIE?

## ...blowing hot and cold!

Whenever there is more than one human-being in any room, there is the possibility that one person will feel differently about the room temperature compared to another. This always amuses me since I thought that unless we were unwell, we were all supposed to have a normal body temperature of between 36.5°C and 37.5°C. I am sure that blood circulation and a whole host of other factors come into it; anyhow it is enough for both you and me to know that it happens, and yes it happens to a greater extent when individuals are in hospital, unwell.

If your loved one has a fever then they will probably be in an isolation unit. In this context I am referring to the general wards shared by patients. It is worth remembering that the position of a patient in a ward of four, for example, may impact on how warm or cool that patient may feel compared to their counterparts.

I have experienced patients who would sit each day by a window, but would feel a draft of air from that window and therefore be colder than a patient who was sitting next to a wall heater. Similarly the open doors on a ward can build up a draft of air that can be very cold to a patient directly in that circulation path.

On each occasion, the patient has always been too cold, rather than complaining of being too hot. I would urge you therefore to give consideration to where your loved-one is seated when you visit them and think about whether they require an extra outer garment for warmth. It is always best for the patient to have the choice of taking off an extra layer of clothing rather than feeling cold. Warmth can be very comforting and therefore psychologically very healing, whereas if one is cold, one can feel downright miserable. Just imagine how much more miserable one feels about this when one is not in one's own home! So, think about whether a cardigan or lightweight jumper is required to be brought in and of course, indelibly ink mark the inside label with their name so that it does not go astray! Encouraging your beloved to put on a cardie could make them feel happier, feel healthier and look stylish too!

# TIP #50 INK SPOTS

## ...signed and sealed!

For at least twenty two years now I have enjoyed writing cards and letters using my fountain pen. The only problem is that I have experienced a few leaks of ink over this period which have either left my hands badly stained...just before an important meeting or has occasionally meant an ink stain on my shirt.

When Mum was in hospital there was an odd time when one of those obstinate ink spots had marked her top. These marks always happen to one's favourite top. To avoid you experiencing any disappointment I decided to share my stain removal treatment with you.

There are so many types of ink compositions now available on the market that there is no one panacea. Writing ink comes in so many forms.

The key to successful stain removal is to identify the spill or leak as soon as it happens. Dried ink is much harder, though not impossible, to successfully remove.

Fountain-pen liquid inks are water-based. If the ink is still wet, then gently blot the stain with a white paper towel or absorbent tissue, positioned both on top of and underneath the stain on the garment. Press very gently and the towels / tissues will soak up the ink. If the ink stain is quite large and you feel that there is more ink to be soaked up then replace the towels / tissues and repeat the process. It is important that the fabric on which the ink mark lies is then gently soaked in cold water. Never use hot water as this will set the stain into the fabric. Once the garment has been rinsed thoroughly in cold water, then take the item home and wash it in lukewarm water as part of a regular wash.

If the stain has not gone after this wash then I would suggest taking the garment to a dry cleaning specialist.

Great care has to be taken because you do not want to damage the garment and render it unwearable.

# TIP #51 HANGING BY A THREAD

## ...a stitch in time!

Once there is an improvement in one's health, the nursing staff may ask the in-patient to arrange for day wear to be brought in. In emergency admissions there is no time to check on whether garments are void of holes and loose threads. It is more important that the person is admitted promptly to hospital.

Once they are settled in, it is worth checking to ensure that all nightwear and day wear for your loved-one is intact and there are no little holes or loose threads dangling. These are not only unsightly but a loose thread could cause someone to trip up by accident.

I hope these personal styling tips inject a new lease of life into your friend and your loved- one to enhance their recovery and make them feel more hopeful and positive about their life! Having covered suggested tips which focus on the person and their own self in the first five chapters, I am now going to share with you in Chapter 6 my tips for Food and Drink.

# CHAPTER 6

## Food & Drink

What we eat and what we drink does matter to our body. Similarly, I cannot put petrol into a diesel car and expect it to work as effectively as diesel. In this chapter, however, I have concentrated the food and drink tips on little things that I hope will make a difference to your loved one or friend while in hospital in an effort to promote their healthy well-being on their journey to a full recovery.

# TIP #52 A NICE CUP OF TEA!

## ...remember to bring milk and teabags!

Both Mum and I were renowned for being a couple of Tea Jennies in hospital. I cannot remember whenever I tasted my first cup of tea, but whether the choice offered is English breakfast, Earl Grey, Chinese or a fruit tea, I have seldom been known to refuse a good cuppa!

One of my friends told me recently that in the UK more than 150 million cups of tea are drunk every day! Goodness only knows how many are served out in hospitals, on airplanes and on trains, let alone the many other outlets such as canteens, restaurants, cafes, bistros and take-away and fast food outlets. It would seem that tea breaks are a tradition that have been with us for many decades if not hundreds of years, whether these are taken from traditional methods of using a teapot and loose tea or perhaps what is more frequently the case nowadays – a brew from a tea bag in a mug!

In hospital, there are standard times for host staff to bring round the tea trolley and indeed in some hospitals there are no such designated staff and the ward nurses and auxiliaries need to take it in turns to serve the morning, evening and afternoon tea!

Back in the 1990's I can remember a most enjoyable afternoon in the elegant Tiffin Room at the legendary and luxurious Raffles Hotel in Singapore. My friend had booked our afternoon tea treat several weeks in advance to avoid disappointment and we spent a most engaging afternoon absorbing the charm and taste of "High Tea".

The atmosphere of the hospital, although devoid of the charm and grand elegance of the Palm Court at the Ritz Hotel in London, was immediately transformed into a frenzy of excitement by my appearance with the bag bearing high quality tea bags, china mugs, sugar, tea spoons and hot water!

Although the ward was not lucky enough to be a member of the Tea Council's exclusive Tea Guild, I remained dedicated to brewing and serving an excellent cuppa every time! There was no extensive selection of different types of tea – loose or bagged – but this personal service in attending to my mother's tea needs was undeniably desirable in its appeal to her, as an alternative break from both the monotony of hospital life and the taste of cheaper tea bags!

You will be delighted to read, no less, that although naturalists recommend the use of a tea bath for the feet at least once a week for around half an hour to help fight bacteria, I did manage to refrained from carrying out this treatment and made sure the used teabags were swiftly put into the bin.

# TIP #53 A LITTLE MORE AGUA!

## ...every Body needs water!

As I was unfamiliar with "hospital life", it took me some time to realise that just because my mother was temporarily lodged in a hospital was no insurance that her level of care received would always be exemplary. This remark was from my own personal observation and is a factual comment stated to be constructive in its delivery. Staffing levels in hospitals at present in many wards, having learned from experience, were understaffed to deliver the quality of personal care and attention that I would have expected for a very vulnerable and mature lady. I frequently encountered the jug filled with water handed out for the personal use of my mother to be left at the back of her bedside cabinet, when she was sitting up in her chair and incapable of reaching for the jug as she pleased. Her impaired mobility did not allow her to get up and pick up the jug of water. My mother's reluctance to be perceived as a "nuisance" in pressing the buzzer to ask for it, meant that she rarely drank any water unless I was present and offered her a glass.

Even when patients are making an excellent recovery, one of nature's basic requirements for humans is to drink water. Every Body needs water!

Water is the most important nutrient that we consume. Water in our bodies affects our circulation, digestion and other key bodily functions. The water to which I am referring, however, is not to be confused with that other wee dram of uisge beatha or "the water of life" given to what we Scots call Scotch whisky!

Whether water or an alternative soft drink is made available to the in-patient, one should actively monitor how much is drunk in your presence as a visitor so that hydration does not become a problem and the in-patient then makes a habit of drinking a little and often. It is then hoped that this practice will become habitual back in their own environment upon discharge.

Equally, to bring non-fizzy drinks and small cartons of fruit juice with a straw attached on the side can provide a tasty alternative to water and those drinks with straws provided negate the need for the patient to buzz for a glass.

# TIP #54 GRAPE EXPECTATIONS

## ...the fountain of youth!

How many of us eat fresh fruit each day? The ancient Greeks even named a God after the grape and its juice, embracing its qualities. In its natural state it is an excellent supplier of energy and nutrition and proffers many medicinal attributes.

The grape seeds are high in antioxidants. What does this mean? Antioxidants are substances that help to prevent free radicals (the by-product of oxidising reactions) from ultimately damaging the cells of our bodies. Pollution, smoking and unhealthy foods are just three sources of free radicals that contribute to a less healthy body.

The body tends to absorb antioxidants better from natural food sources. Fresh grapes contain bountiful numbers of antioxidants that are called polyphenols. These can protect the arterial walls from damage, for example, from a plaque formulation on the walls of the arteries which may suppress blood flow to the heart.

So what are the benefits of eating grapes?

- essential nutrients contained in grapes include vitamins A, B complex, C and K, calcium, iron, magnesium and selenium;
- grapes provide a quick energy boost to the body because of their high sugar content;
- the consumption of grapes has a protective effect on the heart and reduces the risk of heart attacks;
- grapes can help maintain eye health;
- grapes are known to stall the onset of various neuro-degenerative diseases;

- grapes promote brain health and improve constipation and digestion issues;
- grapes also increase the moisture content in the lungs and can also reduce asthma problems;
- grapes help strengthen the body's immune system to destroy cancer cells.

These are just some of the benefits associated with grapes. Apparently, I heard it on the grapevine, there have been recent studies conducted that consider that the enzymes contained in grapes slow down the ageing process. This has implications for potentially extending one's lifespan!

These spectacular health benefits are before one considers the basic need of mankind – the need to drink water. Grape content is at least 70% water. In France it is not an uncommon occurrence for individuals to use the fresh grapes during the grape season as their only diet for several days. While I would not recommend this extreme approach, I would recommend eating more grapes for those of you like me who find it difficult to drink lots of water. These luscious little beads of grapes are packed with wholesome goodness in their natural state without the risks of drinking alcohol. They are easy to digest, great for a quick fix to controlling hunger pangs rather than reaching for a bar of chocolate, and are also relatively inexpensive! Next time you take your loved one or friend a bead of grapes, remember not to eat them all yourself!

# TIP #55 TAKE A TOFFEE

## ...but avoid being toffee-nosed!

Most of the hospitals have either a voluntary staffed shop within the hospital that keeps restricted hours (dependent upon the number of volunteers) or a manned one that is open from early in the morning until about 8pm at night. These little shops are marvellous for buying last minute treats like magazines, sandwiches and chocolate. Although there is quite a few now that stock an inexpensive line of sweets, there is not always the range of product lines that are offered in larger confectionery premises. As a special treat, therefore, and as a change from routine selections available, it is a good idea to take in some toffee. Why? Well, when the days are long in hospital it gives the patient something to chew on and pass more time! Now I know that toffee contains sugar and butter, but a little treat could just be the "pick-me-up" that your loved one needs. If you are feeling very generous you could make your own. There is quite a selection of toffee choices – biscuit toffee, toffee apple, toffee pudding and Moffat toffee, which is not a toffee...most confusing!

When I was twelve years old I was lucky enough to go to camp just outside Moffat for a week's horse-riding. Wonderful! I am passionate about many things and one of them is horses! Anyway, one of the advantages of going into the town of Moffat is finding a shop that sells Moffat toffee! Remarkably, for those uninitiated among you, Moffat toffee is not a toffee. It is a boiled sweet made from a family recipe that produces sweets that are patterned and coloured black and white. They have a tangy, sweet centre that gives them a unique flavour. Mmmm delish!

# TIP #56 A SPOON... AND THE REST

## ...just a spoonful of sugar!

I am not trying to spoon-doggle you with my innocent charm, but merely encouraging you gently to avoid resting on your laurels when you go and visit someone in hospital. In order for the patient to be "right as nine pence" once more, it takes preparation, dedication and motivation to think through the many things with which they may need help. And a spoon is just one such thing! Even if your friend or loved one only drinks black tea or black coffee, there may still be a need to use a spoon if you take in your own hot water and drinks sachet... so that you can stir up the drink. Do not think that because no sugar is taken, or no milk is drunk with tea or coffee that a spoon will be redundant!

The drop of a spoon from the kitchen drawer before you leave for visiting could be just the silver lining necessary to avoid long queues at the nurses' station or outside the ward kitchen during visiting times, waiting for a staff member to fetch one for you. Even a trek to the hospital canteen or café could take up valuable visiting minutes that your patient is keen to spend with you, not without you, while you chase such a serving utensil.

# TIP #57 GLASS IS CLASS

## ...carry the can!

One way to uplift an afternoon soiree is to make the effort to take in a glass for a soft drink as an alternative to a paper cup or a plastic container normally used in the hospitals! Provided the patient is supervised there should be no problem with glass being introduced to the ward as a health and safety issue!

At a glance, it amazed me just how many different types of beverage drinking vessels there are: beakers, tumblers, goblets, quaichs, wine glasses, mugs, tankards, teacups of course, not to mention a variety of beer glassware and other stemware. Let's remember the highball glasses for the cocktails, girls!

Just for once, take in a couple of ordinary table glasses. These are more difficult to break than other drinkware due to their form and hardness. As a traditional table glass has fourteen facets, it is less prone to slip from one's hands and it is also less likely to be broken than other glasses if it is to hit the floor. These can be wrapped up in a clean tea-towel and put in a carrier bag for safe travel.

The opportunity for a change to enjoy a soft drink from a glass rather than an aluminium can will put a smile on your loved one's face, as a treat alternative to other forms of drinkware. Aluminium may be one of the most cost-effective materials to recycle but personally, I would much prefer to taste my drink from a glass container with class! Notably, many consumers find the taste of a drink from a can to be different from drinks drunk from a glass. All in all, our taste receptors are each very different.

For those instances when a tea or coffee is purchased from the local hospital canteen or café, then a useful tip is to ask for a cup sleeve to reduce the heat in holding one of their frequently used single walled paper cup containers. On one occasion I thought

I would be clever and manage to carry two paper cups up two flights of stairs to Mum's ward. As soon as I reached the elevator, my hands felt too hot to hold the cups, as they were not made with an extra layer of insulation to keep both the drink warmer and my hands cooler!

For those of you who are especially organised and who would like the latest "must have" product, may I suggest the 10-ounce porcelain travel cup with lid!

# TIP #58 NUTRITIONAL NUGGETS!

## ...a cereal filler!

Sometimes loss of appetite comes with being a patient. Hospitals may have in-house catering teams or opt to bring in outside caterers. Either way, hospitals can easily be catering for up to 1500 patients or more on a daily basis.

The logistics of transporting the food from either a main kitchen or a courier van and delivering it hot to numerous wards that may be some distance away is very challenging. Thanks to technological wizardry there are numerous meal options available to hospital caterers ranging from hot-line and cook-serve to cook-chill and cook-freeze! Technology is also increasingly relied upon to minimise delays in the serving of hot meals. Added to this is the choice of use of fresh and seasonal ingredients and whether meals require to adaptation for cultural preferences! It all sounds rather pie in the sky to me, but I want to make sure my Mum is not left eating a pig in a poke!

When the food served on hospital wards is of a different cuisine or style to the food choices that would otherwise be made by the in-patient if they were in their own home, then this can be a reason for them not eating their full meal. The menu options on the ward are not as tasty as home-made cooking, are sometimes lacking in flavour and often do not look appetising to the eye. While it is a general rule in most hospitals that visitors are unable to visit on the ward during meal times, during the latter stages of my mother's life I used to leave the ward just as the food trolley was arriving and so I was able to experience first hand the look of the meals served to in-patients.

Individuals like James Martin have started to change the way hospital cuisine is prepared and cooked for the benefit of in-patients across many hospitals. To the extent that in some cases the financial costs are also now reduced when compared to traditional methods and menus adopted is probably a greater encouragement for operational managers to consider the changing food habits; we, as a nation, do not spend sufficient time and pay attention to our general health and food intake even when we are apparently healthy. Each of us, and I include myself in this category, needs to make more time to look after the powerful machine that is our body and wake up to the fact that we cannot drive a car without fuel and so why do we choose to neglect looking after our bodies even when we are not in hospital! Are we so arrogant that we honestly think nothing will happen to us! If you are lacking the motivation or declaring that you are too tired and too busy to change your food habits then STOP! Fifteen minutes of thought can be all the change you need to positively enhance your nutritional life. As my mother would say, "We are a long time dead!"

I have already mentioned how grapes can offer positive benefits. My suggestion is to pay more attention to the ingredients shown on the labels of food and to avoid processed food whenever you can. It is common sense to me that my mother's generation is now living longer than any previous generations because they were not brought up on processed food. Plenty of salads and fresh vegetables always go down well. If you have a craving for a particular food, then find out more about why this might be. Apparently, food cravings can often be the result of food intolerance, candida or hypoglycaemia, but I am no expert on this and suggest you conduct your own research and ask your own questions to your local pharmacist or GP when in doubt.

Now back to your loved one or friend on the hospital ward. Just in case they are hungry due to a loss of appetite when the food trolley came round then I would also suggest taking them in some fruit, plain yoghurt without lots of additives or even a small tub of fresh vegetables like raw carrot chopped up with some celery. This will help to fill a gap and is a healthier option than biscuits and cake when you know that they have either not eaten or eaten very little at standard meal times. If you want to take in some walnuts or almonds be careful to check first that the in-patient does not have any known allergy to them.

There were always some days when my mother was feeling very hungry. I never questioned her much on this but having photographed some of the food that had been left for her to eat it was easy to tell why!

It is always thoughtful to take in a little food just in case your family member or friend has not enjoyed their main meal food or is just feeling like something different to eat. The ease with which the food can be eaten should be considered and if this is fresh fruit, then make sure it is thoroughly washed.

I would find that because my mother was in her eighties, then it only took a little food to help fill her up. A small container of yoghurt with fruit or cereal crunch can be very tasty. Incidentally, I have been told that black-eyed peas are high in fibre, high in protein and low in fat!

# TIP #59 MISSING (WINE) GUMS GONE?

## ...sweet surprise!

One of the sweet treats that my mother has enjoyed for many years is the traditional wine gum. The fact that modern wine gums cease to be made with fermented wine had long escaped my mother's mind. She found the chewy, pastille-type sweets ideal for popping into one's pocket on long walks and always believed that the gelatin content was perfect for growing and strengthening nails. On that count my mother had the most beautifully shaped long nails so I could never disagree with her on that point. My favourites to this day are the red and black gums for preferred flavour.

I would take a small plastic pot filled with wine gums in to her and leave them on top of her bedside cabinet. On one occasion I was disappointed to come into the ward at visiting time and find that the pot filled with the wine gums was missing!

The nurses on duty were asked and I thoroughly checked the cabinet, top middle, bottom and underneath and behind, but there was none to be seen.

It was the next day when one of the other nurses pointed out to me that she had found them in another patient's bedside cabinet! Surprisingly there remained some wine gums in the pot.

The lesson here is to have patience when items go missing, as there frequently is a good reason for their disappearance. If I had thought to put my mother's name on a label on the underside the tupperware pot, then she may have received the sweets back sooner. Always keep an eye on what is left for the patient and help them keep track of things.

A number of years ago my boyfriend had bought me a large box of Black Magic chocolates. It was the holiday weekend and we both sat down to a film with the chocolate surprises. Unfortunately, our surprise was that his favourite montelimar nougat chocolate from the selection was missing. We checked the picture gallery of sweets and their flavours numerous times but it was definitely not shown. The rest of the evening was spent writing a poem about the missing montelimar chocolate. We sent it off to the Marketing Director and within a few days they sent us an apology and two enormous boxes of chocolates as a goodwill gesture to appease our disappointment! Sweet!

Of each of the tips mentioned in this chapter, I feel compelled to remind you of the importance of water. Many of us who consider that we are healthy still suffer from an occasional headache, for example, and yet this may often be the body simply telling us that we need to drink more water to make it effectively function. Do you remember the diesel car that I mentioned at the start of this chapter? Well, if there is one fact I recall from biology class at school it is that the average adult human body is made up of about 60% of water. Why do we expect our body to withstand all the demands that we make of it, when we do not feed it the basic ingredient – water. Ok, now that I have expressed myself I invite you to think about the wider implications of how your loved one or friend feels in hospital after having had their food and drink requirements taken care of, but find they have to spend yet another 24 hours in the same place! Combating boredom on the ward for the duration of one's hospital visit will be considered in the next chapter, entitled Entertainment.

# CHAPTER 7

## Entertainment

How often do you get fed up or anxious if you have to stay in the house for more than 48 hours? Can you imagine how demoralising and stressing this must be for an individual to spend 48 hours in the same room, in a less than full healthy condition, in an unfamiliar environment, shared with strangers with all their little habits, coughs and noises! This is before thought is given to the various nurses, doctors and consultants who under no consultation with you suddenly decide to come up to you and conduct various test checks on your condition, often leaving noisy machinery next to your bed which is necessary as part of the recovery process. You guessed it, on occasion, it can be unbearable! This chapter's tips seek to help address and alleviate some of the boredom and anxiety that your friend and loved one may experience as they are in hospital doing their best to get well.

# TIP #60 ONE MUG OR TWO?

## ...just bring the old china!

Having harped on about tea and spoons, let's remember to bring the mugs! One of my mother's hobbies was to collect a china mug from every tourist town that she visited and so I had plenty of choice from which to choose when I was preparing for each hospital visit.

The reason I suggest this idea, is because often the host for the ward will either not be on duty throughout visiting hours or will be otherwise engaged with other duties. Taking along one's own mugs can make the occasion more special and allows one to avoid being dependant on other staff for anything. Remember that there are many patients in the ward and the ward staff will most likely be rushed off their feet.

If you know your friend or family member has a liking for tea or coffee, then I would take them a fine bone china mug. Somehow the refreshment will taste better from this material as it is an excellent insulator. I normally wrapped both mugs inside a tea-towel for safety when travelling.

One of my friends was invited to The Championships at Wimbledon in 2010 and sent me two commemorative mugs from this prestigious venue. They arrived in time for me to take them up to the hospital and for Mum and I to watch Mum's favourite tennis player, Raphael Nadal, play in the quarter finals scheduled for one afternoon. This was the ace up my sleeve!

Instead of taking fresh flowers or fresh fruit as a gift, why not take your friend or loved one a beautiful fine bone china mug. This type of present is personalised and lasting and can bring much joy from its use. If they have a particular fondness for sport, animals or gardening, for example, then you can buy a fun and colourful mug. These are all generally dishwasher and microwave safe. The additional benefit from this is that the decorated mug becomes a talking point and can bring a smile or a laugh when conversation might otherwise be stale.

Another great choice is to buy a "photo mug". These are easy to create and unique. Ten years ago I had forgotten my skiing escapades in Italy. I received a small carefully packaged box in early autumn and on opening it found to my surprise two photo mugs with photographs of me falling down the Italian Alp ski slopes in Cervinial It was hilarious because I was trying to look really cool and then lost my balance. My friends were already waiting for me at the foot of the slopes and had their mobile cameras at the ready. When I took the mugs into the hospital that afternoon to show Mum it not only gave me another topic of conversation to enjoy with her but it gave both of us a good laugh too!

If you are visiting a child in hospital then perhaps this is a surprise gift they might enjoy and you could even fill the mug with a few sweets.

Perhaps they collect china as a hobby and would be thrilled at the thought of receiving a Commemorative Fine Bone China Mug!

# TIP #61 MUSIC AND CHAIRS

## ...are you sitting comfortably?

Very often in hospital it is not possible to have a bed in a room to oneself. This means that there will be a requirement to share a room. Even when people are brought together to recover from their particular illness, it is possible to create an environment of camaraderie in the ward. This team spirit may help the individuals want to help one another as they feel that they do not want to let each other down.

By thinking about the personal stake of others and asking, "What do they need?" it will be easier to keep people happy and help them to heal faster from their ailments.

Chairs and music are frequently a scarcity when it comes to visiting times. Any opportunity to share both of these is welcomed and to be able to sit in a chair for at least some of visiting time, as one is not allowed as a visitor to sit on the in-patients bed, is ideal.

# TIP #62 STARE GAZING

## ...when bored with nothing to do!

*Staring at the emptiness can seem a pointless task*

*But when I am alone and scared, this practice is a mask*

*To hide all fears, forget one's pain*

*Wishing I was once more home again.*

Next time you visit a ward, spend a moment noticing the in-patients who are sitting and staring into space! There probably will be quite a few. Boredom will have set in. There may not be a television or a regular supply of newspapers and magazines to look at. The best some patients can hope for is a few friendly words from the nursing staff or another patient.

Fortunately, although my mother undoubtedly fell into this category at times when I was unable to be with her to engage in conversation, she was a naturally sociable person with a great sense of humour and wit who attracted attention to brighten up her day.

Spare a thought for those patients who are not feeling well enough or who are not naturally social, outgoing individuals who would like to have their minds stimulated a little more. If you have a spare newspaper or a magazine that you have finished with, think about bringing it into hospital and leaving it for someone who is able to read and who does not normally have a visitor. Maybe you have a paperback book that you no longer need that someone else might enjoy reading.

When I visited my mother on a Sunday there was a remarkable 92 years young lady who loved to read. I used to buy the Sunday Times newspaper and take it in for her to read because it covers such a broad spectrum of news and topics from autos to travel, finance to fashion. It lasted her the whole week!

# TIP #63 SAY IT WITH OR WITHOUT FLOWERS

## ...with bated baby's breath!

The gift of beautiful, fresh flowers always makes me elicit a smile and makes me feel better, even when I feel at my best!

Yet, hospital officials over recent years have been criticised for banning bedside flowers because they pose a "health and safety" risk. From all that I can gather, the procedures for dealing with flowers vary from ward to ward and from hospital to hospital.

This stems from the fact (no pun intended) that attitudes of patients and medical staff towards hospital flowers differ. Some ward staff consider that caring for the flowers takes too much time away from their more practical duties not to mention water spillages, the risk of infection from the flower water or the occasional vase being knocked over!

I personally do not know of any evidence that flower water has ever caused hospital acquired infection?

Just a few years ago, my mother was most upset when, after arranging for a beautiful bouquet of flowers to be sent to her dear sister in hospital, some four hundred miles away, that the ward did not accept flowers.

As a suggestion I would urge you to curb your enthusiasm to purchase these wondrous blooms until you have first checked whether the ward will accept flowers!

I was fortunate with Mum's experience as most of the wards in which she stayed permitted flowers. I took in my own vase into the ward on most occasions, one that I was happy to leave in the ward permanently, and made a point of tidying up the stems and changing the water on a frequent basis.

Although my mother really appreciated the gift of a gorgeous bouquet that included scented lilies, it probably makes sense not to take your family relative or friend flowers that are too heavily scented. For one, they make not like the fragrance, two, they may find it over-powering and start coughing, and three, unless you are in a private ward, there may be other patients sharing the ward who either have hay fever or who do not like the particular scent selected.

The power of flowers is diminished as a welcome gift if they fail in their objective to make someone happier!

If you are disappointed that ward staff refuse to have natural flowers on their ward, then consider saving your surprise until your friend or relative returns home. As a last resort to add some colour and cheerfulness to any ward, you could choose to take in some artificial daffodils or tulips. I noticed that one lady had done this for a patient in one of my mother's neighbouring wards. The yellow of the daffodils throughout winter brought a cheery disposition to those patients and their visitors to the ward, without the threat of infection or maintenance!

# TIP #64 MODERN HEART!

## ...fond flirting!

The hospital environment and support services should support a certain quality of care for all people, and especially the older, more vulnerable individuals. Despite the segregation of men from women on the wards, my mother still managed to enjoy fond flirtations with the young art teacher and enjoy the support services offered.

Once in the rehabilitation unit, certain limited activities were provided for the more alert, active patients of mind and spirit. One such activity was the art class on a Tuesday and Thursday morning. Prior to the start of each class, the art teacher would frequent the wards to establish if there was any interest in the art class that day. My mother had mentioned the class to me several times but had been nervous about attending herself. I suggested that one morning I would come up to the hospital and accompany her to the class. It was a very calming, peaceful environment conducive to promoting creativity and mind stimulation. Beautiful classical music wafted around the art room and teas and coffees were offered. My mother happily looked through a few books on dance, theatre and wildlife. At first she was looking for ideas for something to draw and so a book of birds with pictures of her favourite barn owls were of great interest to her. One of the other ladies present was over a hundred years young and very alert. She had a marvellous mischievous glint in her eye that suggested she had thoroughly enjoyed most of her life. She looked a real character and was chattering away to the art teacher as she busily selected another colour for the butterflies she was painting. All in all it was a most illuminating experience. After the art class I wheeled Mum back to the ward and settled her into her space. Within seconds I was laughing gregariously when she said to me that she didn't think the young art teacher was "her type" and she hoped he would not be offended!

Clearly the art lesson was stimulating all the senses. Seek to reconnect with your purity of heart in whatever way you feel is right for you!

# TIP #65 LET'S DANCE

## ...twist and shake!

None of us needs a reason to dance, but how many of us have done any dancing recently? How many times have you have listened to a piece of music on the radio and started involuntarily to tap your foot or beat the rhythm out with your hand?

I am not advocating we all take up our Motivators and instantly dance the samba or do zumba moves. I am suggesting that we are motivated to indulge in a few light dance moves to benefit us in a range of ways: to keep one's mind alert; to shake off stiffness of the arms, legs and other muscles; to improve flexibility; as a means of self-expression to cheer us up when we are feeling frustrated or a little low and the overriding reason – to have fun!

My mother was in a wheelchair for most of her stay in hospital. She found herself able to wiggle her toes and rotate her swollen feet in both a clockwise and anti-clockwise direction to keep the joints less stiff. Even when one's shoulders are a little stiff, it is most likely that your loved-one will be able to raise their arms out and up a little to improve circulation. In my yoga class my teacher regularly makes us take time to stand with our arms at shoulder level. We then take it in turn to bend the arm in towards the chest, hold the one hand level and then using the other hand we gently pull and wiggle each part of each finger, one at a time.

All of these small actions can add up to making us feel good. By encouraging your loved- ones to participate in these activities is to allow both them and you to feel the love!

# TIP #66 LET ME ENTERTAIN ME

## ...sing to yourself!

For as long as I can remember my mother always sang. She sang me to sleep, she sang whilst doing tedious housework and she sang in the church choir. Why then would she not sing in hospital?

Music can be very inspiring and it has long been known that music can be a great contributory factor to the overall healing process. It is a truly powerful medium and can make us feel instantly different in a positive, uplifting way when we listen to it or sing out.

Due to the long hours one endures in hospital, can I suggest that a little singing to yourself does no harm, and probably will do you a power of good. It helps to lift your mood and to help you breathe better, exercising your diaphragm and vocal chords.

I inherited my mother's fondness for singing and have sung in front of audiences since I was five years old. With all that has happened over the last few years I have not practised my singing enough, but what I am sure of is that whenever I have felt a little low, selecting a favourite song to sing to has always been the catalyst to change my mood to a much happier one and for making me feel much more grateful about all aspects of my life – the highs and the lows. Music can really bring people together and allows an individual to be 'in the moment' with music they are either listening to or actively involved in playing or singing, such that they forget any worries that they may have in that moment.

Music gives individuals a chance to express themselves and to release any tension. I believe it can truly make you feel that you can achieve anything at all. It can be pivotal to improving someone's life experience and well-being. Music knows no barriers and can be enjoyed by everyone no matter how unwell they are. There is no need to be able to read sheet music either. My mother was told when she was very young that had she not suffered diphtheria she could have become a professional opera singer. It did not stop her singing in the bathroom, the kitchen, the garden and well, the list continues...Lol! I am lucky in that I have inherited her love for singing and fondness for music, but to date I cannot read sheet music either and learn by ear too.

Sometimes in the hospitals there is a hospital radio station set up by dedicated teams of volunteers specifically for audio broadcasting for the benefit of the in-patients of hospitals. I was involved in such a Glasgow hospital radio station for a couple of years and found it very enjoyable both to play special requests and also to meet the in-patients and cheer them up with their favourite song.

For the lucky ones among you, you may already have an iPod, smartphone or tablet computer that you could listen to and sing along with too!

# TIP #67 BOOK YOUR NEXT VISIT

## ...a date with Dickens!

My grandfather very kindly gave me a collection of Dickens novels that I read when I was in my teenage years and they still retain that wonderful old smell about them, whenever I pick one up to read. The point is that reading is a wonderful pastime that you can do yourself. Hours spent in hospital can be made more joyful by losing yourself in a good book!

This is also a great way to take some of the perceived pressure off your relative and friends, who will not feel so guilty if they struggle to visit you frequently, but know that you have much to keep you occupied.

Many hospitals have a small bookcase or library from which patients can choose books to read. This can save a special request being made to your visitors.

There is no excuse to delay reading a book as even for those with partial or full sight loss, there are audio books too. Magnifying glasses are also available if you think your current spectacle prescription is due for renewal or the light on the ward is poor and you struggle to read with clarity.

Ah! Those good old bedtime story sessions with Mum – what fun!

And for those of you who poopoo traditional books feel free to take out your tablet or iPad and download an eBook. I have heard that "Feel the Love" is trending just now! Lol!

# TIP #68 IN THE PINK

## ...indulge a pink lady!

Although I am keen on gardening...when I am in the mood... this tip is nothing to do with the Dianthus flower, many varieties of which are called Pinks. Nor is it a reference to either a classic gin-based cocktail or a Japanese female pop duo of the late 1970s and early 1980s!

It is instead a suggestion to appeal to the basic need of a human-being to feel good about themselves, whatever that may mean. Only when you take the time to really listen and get to know a person will you find out what that is. For some, a short time is all that is needed. For others it can take a lifetime to really know what another person likes, simply because we have forgotten the art of communication and of expressing how we feel. Unless you are one of the fortunate ones who already knows what makes your relative or friend feel good about themselves, what better opportunity to start this journey of discovery right now. Speak your truth! Be honest at this very vulnerable time of ill health and let the natural love flow among your friends and loved ones. But, equally, be ready for unexpected responses and words spoken as a result. The truth can often appear to be hurtful, when really once the emotive element is removed from the comment or thought, the true reality of a feeling or situation can be revealed that is very cathartic and most healing! Remember that to find oneself in hospital is often misunderstood as a need for the healing of only the physical ailments and maladies. The truth is that at a deeper level there are often very deep emotional scars that require to be healed too. Choose this precious "downtime" to listen to yourself and to look in the mirror at who you really are. You may be surprised at how good you then feel. Choose this time to make peace with your past, so it will not mess up your future. Don't compare yourself to others. You have no idea what their journey is all about. This is about your time for feeling better in your world! Being in the peak of health includes feeling in peak condition, and only you will know when you have reached that state of contentment. Meantime, let others help you to feel "in the pink" and to be "tickled pink", by sharing with them some of your thoughts, truths and desires. Whatever makes you happy!

# TIP #69 WHAT ABOUT DRAUGHTS?

## ...game on!

Board games for the bored! Why not play a game of draughts for a change?

I know that it is possible to play such strategic board games as draughts on line, but in hospital this opportunity is rare and so the next best thing is to take in the board and the play pieces carefully in a box or bag and set it up either on a table in the day room or on the patient's tray table and enjoy a game!

For those of you who prefer to exercise your strategic brain harder then there is chess. A favourite of mine!

If neither chess nor draughts is appealing then revert to a pack of playing cards. These packs are easy to carry and can provide just as much fun and amusement.

My all time favourite game as a child was playing Bezique and Rubicon Bezique, although sadly I have not played this for many years. I used to play it with my 95 years young grandfather and when he passed away I never played it again. Now it has been so long I have forgotten the rules!

While both the games of draughts and chess require two players, one can happily amuse oneself with a pack of cards and play Patience for hours!

# TIP #70 BACK-PAGE INSPIRATIONS

## ...competitions!

My great aunt was an avid crossword puzzle solver. She would enjoy filling in at least one puzzle daily and she bought a crossword puzzle magazine too. As I am not keen on them myself, it was not until I spotted a lady in the bed opposite my mother one day, asking the nurse for a specific magazine that I realized she took great enjoyment from filling in puzzles...of all kinds.

If crosswords are not for you, then there is a terrific choice of other puzzles and riddles to keep your brain fit: sudoku, anagrams, word play, trivia, word searches, riddles, logic puzzles, cryptograms and doublets. All these games and I have not mentioned Mahjong yet either.

There can be much to do when in hospital but we owe it to the care of our friends and relatives to think for them and consider choices to give them that will help them positively throughout their stay.

# TIP #71 SURROUND SOUND

## ...play to the gallery!

There is never much privacy in hospital unless you are fortunate to have a private room. It was Shakespeare who said, "if music be the food of love, play on."

I mentioned previously in my book about the wonderful impact music can have. Singing is one direct activity, but the more passive behaviour of listening to music can be very therapeutic and relaxing too. It can also stir up instant feelings of irritation if you do not like a certain style of music. Very emotive! Very powerful! Music has a tremendous universal pulling-power and can transport you back to places and past times quicker than any other stimuli.

When my mother first went into hospital I thought that she would miss listening to her favourite music channels on Sky, and so I took her in a small television and cd player. She was not so bothered about missing the television channels but she did enjoy listening to a selection of music, from classical sonatas to current pop music. Incidentally, it was always my mother, even as an octogenarian, who kept me informed of which pop artist or group was number one in the charts!

Looking around the ward, the shut eye syndrome had taken effect. By consciously standing up and asking if anyone would like to listen in to the music, pairs of eyes slowly started to open and the energy from the music playing, began a life of its own.

Similarly, if someone else on the ward has a music system they are using, respectfully ask them if they would be willing to turn the sound up. This can be entertainment for all.

I do hope that among these various entertainment tips that you have found at least one that you think will give a little pleasure and delight to your friend and loved one. Of course, aside from reducing the boredom from staying in hospital there is the more serious side to the recovery process. Is your friend and loved one becoming mentally, emotionally and physically stronger each day and feeling more like their usual self again? Is this in-patient progress being recognised by the medical staff? In Chapter 8 Patient Progress I take a look at tips for assisting the healing process.

# CHAPTER 8

## Patient Progress

The recovery process of an in-patient depends on many different factors. I am unqualified and unable to speak on the medical factors. I am, however, able to offer tips on all the other esoteric stuff that no matter how small the effort made is, can often make a difference to your friend or loved one as part of their overall healing experience.

# TIP #72 A FIREMAN'S LIFT

## ...professional support!

When the in-patient has experienced major trauma, surgery or has suffered broken bones then there will be times when although they are attempting to do more things for themselves, as a visitor you will neither be experienced nor physically able to assist your friend or relative. An example of this may be while you are visiting and the in-patient requires help to sit up in their bed or in their chair. When you see them struggling to do this on their own then it is best to call for professional assistance from one of the trained hospital staff to avoid you damaging yourself and puling any muscles. Not all recovery will happen overnight and so be patient and do not be too proud to ask for help when it is needed.

# TIP #73 GOODNIGHT KISS

## ...kissing games!

Kisses are wonderful expressions of greeting, respect and affection.

I believe that in certain circumstances no-one can ever have enough kisses, but then I am probably more passionate than your average person! And I strongly suggest that you certainly do not always seek to kiss someone that you don't know!

Aside from the lover's kiss and the romantic kisses that we are lucky enough to enjoy from an intimate or close relationship, I am talking here about a lip salute to show fondness and genuine caring for the person you are visiting in hospital, often in the view of others. Sadly, expressing visible emotion has not been the diktat of the average British person.

A word of caution, therefore, for some people are traditionally non-tactile individuals who are not used to neither lavishing praise and affection on others or indeed, having the affection lavished on themselves. While one person may find it very natural to greet another person on the cheek, to another they may distinctly dislike it, and only a formal handshake may be acceptable. Public displays of affection are sometimes frowned upon. In these circumstances, I would recommend starting off with an air kiss as a more acceptable form of social kissing. This is also extremely helpful when one wears bright red lipstick, because it avoids physical contact with your friend or family member and so preserves one's lippy! It generally involves the lightest brush past of the cheek.

When I left Mum in hospital each night we would enjoy throwing one another kisses with our hands as I disappeared out of the ward. This is a playful, innocent gesture of affection and seldom offends anyone present.

For those of you who are keen to take things further, social kissing etiquette can be thoroughly digested in Debrett's Etiquette Book.

# TIP #74 EARLY ONSET OF DEMENTIA

## ...you've already told me that!

It was not until I had visited my Mum on one specific occasion at afternoon visiting, that I realised she had a mild forgetfulness. The sun was shining brightly and there was barely a cloud in the sky. As I strode into the hospital ward she was smiling in her wheelchair waiting for me to arrive. If I was a few minutes late she often mentioned that my lateness cut into her visiting time stating that it was short enough as it was without being further curbed by me. An accurate statement succinctly put!

When I then proceeded to ask her what she had been up to in the morning she told me that she had been for a long walk down to the shops and had had a really pleasant time. At that moment, I knew that there had been many occasions when my mother had mentioned little things that didn't quite stack up. On this occasion I knew unquestionably that my mother had not left the hospital ward and definitely had not been for a beautiful long walk down to the local shops as she had mobility challenges and was wheelchair bound. This specific incident made me realise going forward that if she was to mention similar 'memories' to me in future, that instead of me spending ten minutes telling her that she couldn't possibly have gone for the walk and slowly spiralling both of us into a bad mood, I would now remain calm and merely comment something like, "Oh that was good. Did you meet anyone you knew?" In this way, it would keep my mother's stress levels at a low and prompt for a happier visiting time with her. I truly believe that she was happy in her world and why would I want to spoil that?

As a secondary note, however, it made me realise that when I reflected on other incidents with Mum both at home and in the hospital that I knew about, perhaps there was a little more to this than a mild forgetfulness. I also was aware that she had encountered the following from time to time:

- a problem finding the right words, not just in hospital but also prior to her hospital stay when she was at home. Whenever this happened both of us used to just laugh it off and she would say, "oh it doesn't matter, anyway. I will remember in a minute." My mother was very clever to cover up her weakness in this area by laughing it off and sometimes making up her own words to suit the occasion which was often really funny;
- a loss of confidence. Initially this started when she did not want to walk into a café or restaurant herself unless I was by her side. Over time this built up to include not wanting to answer the front door or having people in the house to help with maintenance problems such as plumbing, painting and decorating;
- forgetting names when she was recounting memories;
- misplacing items and putting them in odd places. On one occasion I had given her my Cartier watch to wear because she adored different time pieces and liked to wear them as statements of jewellery rather than solely as a means to tell the time. When I asked her one evening where my watch was kept she point blank refused to acknowledge that she had even seen it and even after describing it to her she again denied ever having seen it let alone having worn it. She became irritable and agitated at me asking the question. The look on her face I now realise was one of frustration at the forgetfulness she was encountering. It was as if part of her knew she should know the answer but simply could not give it. I let the matter drop because she was getting so anxious and inwardly annoyed with herself. It was about eight months after my mother passed that I

eventually found my watch carefully tucked away in the inside zip pocket of one of her old handbags that she had not used for years.

I would say that if you are aware of any of these symptoms sounding familiar to your circumstances then do not be afraid to ask for help.

Sometimes brain cells stop working properly and this can develop into a wider issue diagnosed as dementia. If you would like to find out more about dementia then I would suggest looking at the website www.alzheimersresearchuk.org.

While millions of people around the world currently suffer from Alzheimer's disease, the most wonderful news is that in 2015 two scientists successfully conducted testing on mice using high frequency sound waves to break down the dreaded plaque, which builds up and builds up until it effectively imprisons certain memory remembrance within the brain. Professor Jürgen Götz is the director of the Clem Jones Centre for Ageing Dementia Research in Australia. For those of you who are keen to read either the abstract of their research study or indeed the full work, it has been published in the journal Science Translational Medicine (Leinenga & Götz,2015).

Science Magazine www.sciencemag.org

Science Translational Medicine

RESEARCH ARTICLE ALZHEIMER'S DISEASE

The reason that I am so excited about this medical and scientific breakthrough is that it focuses on physics as a potential and possible solution to such a debilitating and heart-wrenching disease. Why the excitement about physics you may ask? Well, think about present day mass medicine! The majority of cures, pain controllers and pain inhibitors all require some form of pill and these pills have been developed using chemistry. My issue with chemistry is that it involves chemicals. By their very nature, chemicals generally have side effects because one is pushing one thing and something else reacts differently and we all know what the worst side effect may lead to!

My confidence is in the science of physics. Physics is the way forward! In my personal opinion the future is not chemicals. so young scientists of the future take note and choose your school subjects wisely!

It should be noted that while this ultrasound research is clearly in its embryonic stages, there is no doubt in my own mind that this alternative way of looking at health cures is going to be the key catalyst in the future for improved health and well-being. In my personal opinion, the way forward is unquestionably through physics and not chemistry. More and more scientists are very slowly realising that the power of physics in our reality from test work done will ultimately lead to changing the traditional laws of physics that we know today and excitingly reveal more wonders about our human existence and the world in which we live. Can you imagine the excitement of working with a new kind of physics, a benevolent physics, that will be able to resist disease and bacteria rather than having to rely on a genetically altered science?

In opening up one's mind both to the acceptance of new knowledge and to new ways of doing things, there is a dearth of potential scientific breakthroughs and opportunities to come, specifically in the field of healthcare, that will transform the lives of many and I am thrilled to be around at this time to see it unfold in its magnificent elegance.

# TIP #75 CENTRAL STATION

## ...not Glasgow...that's just the ticket!

When Mum was first admitted to hospital I can remember I was given a leaflet telling me about the ward staff practices and various uniforms to differentiate one staff member from another and yet, despite my business background and professional discipline, somehow it all just seemed one BIG blur!

For years I had studied copious notes to pass numerous exams. Suddenly, I found it impossible to remember the status of one uniform colour and badge from another. Honestly, I did not care about the importance of recognising a staff nurse from an auxiliary. All I cared about was the improved health condition of my Mum.

Within hours I had found myself thrust into a different world about which I knew nothing! Ordinarily, I would not blink an eye to visiting a new business and conducting an overview assessment of policies, practices and business processes, providing advice on how to strategically plan for future years improved profits and cash flow generation whilst streamlining processes and managing productivity levels accordingly. So what was the problem this time? Emotions. MY emotions. Fear, exasperation and frustration had set in and would take me on a roller-coaster journey of discovery of this new world!

Rather than attempt once more to digest the hospital leaflet, I observed other visitors and decided to ask questions at the central nurses' station on the ward. This is the area around which all staff at some point congregate to update patient records, timetable patient care needs and generally manage the full care programme for each patient. There is invariably an informal queue of visitors throughout visiting hours waiting to ask their own important questions, but I found this to be the best way to be kept informed of the patient's care needs.

If you are visiting a patient that has mild forgetfulness or is either in the early stages of dementia or has been identified as having dementia, then often they will not remember conversations with medical staff about their condition or they may remember incorrectly the information that has been imparted to them. For peace of mind it does not take long to check at the central station and hear progress directly from a nurse.

# TIP #76 DOCTOR ON THE GO!

## ...in the house!

When you are unsure about the care plan of your friend or relative and you are not of a medical background yourself, then it can seem hugely complex, complicated and worrying not to know what is going on. In order to understand the various charts and in-patient records that are left in a folder at the foot of the bed, then I would suggest that a few words with the in-patient's doctor would be helpful to give clarity to the situation where you have not been able to ascertain the reason for your friend or loved one's admission to or on-going treatment in hospital.

At one time, there was a joke that the hospital porters would go missing hiding in cupboards to avoid their work routines. Now the joke is still told but the spot-light is on the hunt for the doctor!

An hour of visiting time can soon go round. If either you or your friend, family member is concerned about something and needs to speak to a medical staff member I would suggest ringing the buzzer in the first instance. If the person you need to speak to is not present, for example, a doctor or consultant, then I would wait until the end of visiting time and then go to the central station and ask for the telephone number of the medical member's P.A. so that you can contact them directly for an appointment. Hospital staff will seldom make an appointment for you without going through the P.A. and this process could save you waiting around and wasting time looking along corridors and in wards for the right person.

You can also ask at the central station to find out when specifically the doctors and consultants would normally undertake their ward rounds. If you have an urgent, specific need and you want to speak to a doctor then ask a medical staff member for the person's P.A. (personal assistant) contact number. This is usually the quickest way to find a doctor who is not on call to your specific ward when you are visiting. If you have a specific question that you would like to ask and you are nervous that you may forget to say everything you need to say then write it down on a piece of paper and put it in an envelope and mark it for the doctor's attention and the in-patient about whom you are asking.

# TIP #77 TIME TO SAY GOODBYE

## ...the bells are ringing, "Oyez!"

Visitors are generally very welcome, but as several hospitals state, do not visit if you are unwell. Assuming that you are a reasonably healthy specimen of humanity and you have successfully made it through the front door, you may find like I did, that visiting time passes all too quickly and before you know it, you are forgiven for thinking you yourself have tinnitus, when you consistently hear ringing in your ears. But wait! Before you rush off to your local doctor for the latest tinnitus cure, listen again and realise that these "chimes" are coming from an outside source – the ward nurse ringing the bell again to signal the end of visiting!

For those of you reading who have studied campanology, my reference to chimes was for effect only. In the interest of providing material that could be perceived as educational, I found myself searching for the many bells that exist throughout the world today and was rather surprised to learn of the sheer variety available – Big Ben (London), the Millenium Peace Bell (America), the Ming Bell (Burma), Czar Kolokol (Russia), the Bell of Beijing (China), Daibasto Temple Bell (Japan), camel bells and the sleigh bell to name just eight.

Now when the nurses talk of change ringing this should not be confused with the traditional English art of ringing a set of tower bells in an intricate series of changes whereby ropes are pulled attached to bell wheels. I am unconvinced that the bell ringing on the ward is ever as well rehearsed as to ring in such mathematical permutations. Apparently in olden times, change ringing was originally a gentleman's recreation from which women were excluded. For those ladies who did participate, it was perceived a mark of social status.

Certainly the female staff members were very keen to ring the bell to end visiting on the ward and although the bell, when swung did not rotate as much as 360 degrees, the hand stroke swing of the bell made it quite clear to all who listened that the (visitors') time was up. It used to amuse me the mood of the person swinging the bell. Sometimes the bell sound was very abrupt and sharp, on other occasions it echoed more like a tolling… a single stationary bell ringing in slow repetition. When the mood of the nursing staff was lighter, it was customary for different staff to take it in turns to ring the bell and in a good mood two nurses would rush to ring the bell and pretend to peal the bell shouting like a town-crier, "Oyez, oyez, oyez!", before pronouncing with their tiny hand-bell that visiting time was over.

A bell's movement is called its "duty," and various methods are identified by the duty given each bell. Whenever it was my duty as a visitor to leave, I would always take my time and eke out a few extra minutes with Mum. My mother had always held vivid memories of her time in a hospital as a four year old suffering from diphtheria in an isolated room with only a small window for her mother to look through at visiting time. She still held on to the fear of hearing the bell ring at the end of each visiting time as a child and seeing her own mother step back from the window, to know only then that it would be another long night and day before she would see her again. This fear of having to say cheerio to me washed across her face every time I visited her and it broke my heart to have to leave.

# TIP #78 RESIST ROAMING

## ...searching for souls!

There are different stages to the recovery of the in-patient. This may mean that your loved one or colleague may be moved to another ward and the staff may omit to inform you in advance that this has happened. You can imagine my complete shock when I arrived at visiting time to the receiving ward soon after my mother had been admitted to hospital only to find that another in-patient was occupying her room. My mind began to race about what had happened to her and at that time I feared the worst until one of the hospital staff informed me that she had been moved to another ward as part of her progress! My mother did not use her mobile phone in hospital and so she had been unable to tell me where she was. That afternoon I wasted the first half hour of visiting time firstly finding out where she was and then secondly attempting to trail around the hospital looking for the new ward! When I did find her my mother had become anxious because I was late for visiting and thought that I had had an accident on the way to the hospital. Not the most calming influence on events to complement the healing process.

On another occasion I was informed that there was a strong possibility that my mother would be moved to another hospital the following day. I specifically told the duty nurse to telephone my mobile number that she had for me to let me know when my mother was going to be transferred the following day in order that I could make my way for afternoon visiting to the correct hospital. I checked the mobile number that she had written down for herself, to minimise the likelihood of a mistake. Needless to say the nurse did call and left a message stating that my mother was going to be transferred but did not tell me when. You guessed it. I arrived at afternoon visiting at the former hospital to be told that she had been transferred to the new hospital.

When I challenged the same nurse she was adamant that she had specifically told me the time in the voicemail left on my phone. As I had retained this I was in a position to play it back to her and let her hear that there was no time mentioned. She was totally unrepentant and without any apology. I ran out of the ward and to my car to drive across to the new hospital to see Mum. I arrived with only ten minutes to spend with Mum that afternoon. Once more, my mother had been upset wondering where I was at visiting time and once more we had lost time to share together. A lesson for all to learn!

# TIP #79 MUST-HAVE APPOINTMENT

## ...the ring of truth!

If you have a serious concern, then usually it can be arranged for you to either phone in during the ward round of the doctor at a prearranged time or for you to turn up at the ward to meet with him privately.

Either way, the onus always has to be on you to make the request to meet with the doctor and to make the appointment. Gone are the days when the doctor will approach you to keep you informed. The only time I have heard of this being done, was when a doctor approached a patient in an open ward to inform her that she had cancer! Where is the dignity and respect according to hospital practice in that! Shocking!

Even if you consider that you have a good memory, it does no harm to take a small notepad and pen to the appointment. In this way you can take a few notes and even write down a few questions in advance of your meeting to make sure that you give yourself every opportunity to ask all of your questions.

If, like me, you have no professional medical knowledge and your loved-one has been admitted to hospital and you do not understand their diagnosis and they do not understand their diagnosis, then please make a point of asking to see the doctor to obtain an explanation that you both understand.

One of my friends sadly found out to her agony and utter devastation, that her father, as an in-patient, had only three weeks to live! She had been visiting her father and neither he nor her understood what the problem was with his health. No-one had ever approached her at visiting time to inform her of his health challenges. After several weeks of her father being in hospital, she finally found a staff member who helped her make an appointment with the consultant. When she finally sat down with the consultant he informed her that her father had only three weeks to live. The consultant was shocked to find out that no other staff member had informed her of her father's health position until that meeting.

The fact that this situation happened on one known occasion is one time too many, in my opinion! As visitors, if we each help our loved-ones then collectively we are empowering each other to push for improved healthcare processes and practices to reduce the likelihood of this type of scenario being repeated.

# TIP #80 SURGERY CONFIDENTIAL

## ...find a private place!

From the first stage of admission to hospital, one can request at any time to speak with the consultant. This is one piece of information that is frequently forgotten about in the trauma of the circumstance.

In my experience, I have been present when a medical staff member discussed my mother's case in the public domain of the open ward – highly unprofessional! Moreover, I have observed this situation arise with other patients and their families and so it is probably more prevalent than one cares to think!

In an unfamiliar environment it is really important that for something as major as the discussion of the patient's ongoing care programme, that ultimate privacy is sought.

The space made available for private meetings with medical staff will vary from hospital to hospital. Do not be put off if no suggestion is made to seek privacy to discuss case notes. Remember to ask for privacy. This may be use of the relative's room, a classroom, a meeting room or the day room, for example. If another patient is occupying the day room and this is the only space free for a meeting, then suggest to the medical staff member that you are excused for ten minutes to respect your privacy. Make this your law unto one's health!

# TIP #81 CALL OF THE CHILD

## ...adult nurturing!

Remember that the hospital environment can be a very fearful place and even the oldest of adults, on occasion, can feel insecure especially when they are unwell. Sometimes an adult patient may withdraw into themselves and feel unable to listen to what the nurses, doctors and consultants have advised them to improve their well-being.

When you are visiting your loved one and friends, colleagues in hospital take the time to observe how they are reacting to their environment and be prepared to step up and be their voice when they are feeling insecure or low. This seemingly small gesture could have a significant on their speed of and quality of recovery. Be their earth angel for a day!

# TIP #82 HOW MUCH DOES IT HURT?

## ...need for painkillers!

Each one of us has a different threshold of pain. Pain is not natural and pain is a signal from our body that something is not right. Pain tolerances can vary across race, sex and age. Different medication can be used to treat different levels of pain severity, but for all instances, the patient has to be the one to ask for pain relief. I did not realise this and in the early days when Mum complained of a few muscular aches I abruptly walked off to find a nurse. I explained the situation to her and when she came back with me to ask my mother if she wanted a painkiller my mother said that it was alright and she would just leave taking anything for just now! I then felt rather foolish as if I had made my mother's condition out to be far worse than it was! Latterly, when such instances arose, I explained to her what I was going to do and that it was her responsibility to ask for pain relief when the nurse came round. I explained that I was not able to ask the nurse on her behalf, as I did for so many other things.

While I believe that every pain medication administered has both advantages and risks, I accept that there are situations when even a mild or moderate pain needs to be treated with a pain relieving drug to make the patient more calm and comfortable.

One of the problems with my mother's generation is that they think to ask a nurse for a painkiller is tantamount to being a nuisance. Alternatively, my mother would be scared to mention that she had even a mild pain in front of a medical staff member, in case she was whisked away for a host of other examinations and for the doctors to establish that they had found something else wrong with her!

A little diplomacy is required by you. The best advice I can offer to you is to observe the overall well-being of your loved-one when you visit them and if they seem anxious or have an unusually short attention span, then ask them how they are feeling. Judge from their answer whether it is worth having a quiet word with one of the nurses on the ward and then they as professionals can monitor the situation and administer any medication as they consider necessary.

# TIP #83 YOU BRUISER!

## ...pour oil on it!

Different surroundings, people, obstacles and medical treatments can all give rise to unexpected incidents occurring, such as falls that leave unsightly bruising.

In my mother's case, she was in need of an intravenous drip for salines to rehydrate her, but she did not have veins that were near the surface of her skin. The distress on her veins from the medical staff finally accessing an appropriate vein left her with serious bruising all round her hand and wrist.

No matter where it is, I find a marvellous treatment for bruising is to gently rub in some warm, extra virgin olive oil all around the distressed area. This was one of my mother's remedies that I regularly pass on to friends and willing participators. Mum, who had no medical qualifications, would tell me that this oil was one of the few oils that penetrated deep into the skin and would "bring out the bruising" to help heal the specific area.

While there may be no historical medicinal reactions to applying olive oil to the skin or direct pharmacological test results proving its worth, I know that it has been used over hundreds of years for a variety of ailments. I would suggest that it is doubtful that enough can be absorbed through the skin to elicit any negative reaction.

Back in the late 1980's, my mother was unfortunate to fracture her shoulder. There was no scope for using plaster, because of the awkward positioning of the break and so for five weeks she had to wear a cumbersome sling – and – swath device to heal the break. She had to sleep sitting up on the sofa for the entire five weeks that the shoulder was healing, propped up appropriately with a selection of pillows and cushions. Every morning and evening either Dad or I would gently massage some hot olive oil around her shoulder area. Once the bruising and swelling had started to subside, then the sporadic itching started. When Mum returned to the doctor for a physical check-up, he was very surprised at the extent of the healing over such a short time for an older person. My mother told him that she had had regular olive oil applied to the arms, shoulder and chest area, to which understandably as a medical doctor, he replied, "Well, if it works for you..!".

Whenever I have gone on a skiing holiday, the first stop once I have reached my destination is to find a local store that sells small bottles of olive oil. Each day after skiing hard and showering, I would apply the oil to my skin. Every morning without fail I would wake up with zero stiffness in my limbs. Absolutely terrific! The first holiday I tried this out I could hardly believe how great I felt the second morning into my ski holiday. All of my other friends were moaning about their aches and pains and we were all in our twenties! I diplomatically kept quiet. On arrival I had given each of them the opportunity to have their own bottle of oil and they had all turned me down. That's ok, too.

# TIP #84 SPACE RAGE

## ...room for improvement!

The poor quality of patient care is never far from my mind when I write about the space rage I felt when my mother was in hospital. There are minimum standards which must be met and these were not adhered to.

Evident weaknesses in space use were prevalent and there needs to be more active engagement of the hospital communities if room for improvement is to be achieved.

I feel sure that there is a correlation between space use and the quality of both the hospital environment and patient care. I wonder whether nursing staff consider the effective and efficient use of space and the furniture in that space to be part of their professional responsibilities.

Managing space is a complex process, but if real improvement in space use is to be made then each individual has to take responsibility for making this happen.

The main problem identified was that my mother, whose mobility was significantly impaired post admission to hospital, was unable to stand up out of her chair. Due to a complete lack of thought from hospital staff, while she was seated in her chair for most of the day on one side of the bed that she used, her bedside cabinet with the drawers containing all of her makeup and toiletries was neatly positioned across the other side of the bed, out of her reach. In short there was a functional mismatch of space utilisation! This did not only deprive my mother of what limited independence that she had left, but it placed a totally unnecessary burden on the nursing staff. Clearly, they were understaffed on the ward without having to answer to the triviality of passing a magazine over to my mother to read from time to time, let alone apply this on one ward potentially another

35 times! I would like to comment that this service was even offered to my mother, but sadly on more than one occasion the magazines that I had specifically brought in for her would go missing and it was common for me to find them being read by the nursing staff at the central station when I came in to visit!

On a frequent basis, I would enter the ward and find that my mother had a water glass on her side table for water, but the jug of water was still full and sitting on top of the bedside cabinet – across the other side of the bed!

Even I know that dehydration is a major problem for older people. How can patients help themselves when the tools are not made available for their own use?

Little patient care, little dignity, no respect!

I am truly surprised that patients do recover and are discharged for home having evidenced some of the poor standards adopted!

So what are the three main issues with regards to space use?

There needs to be more emphasis placed on the following quality factors:

- Information – ensure that ward staff are made responsible for thinking about the basic needs of a patient in relation to the positioning of furniture;
- Design – remodel the space to meet the needs of the patient and enable access to their cabinets;
- Communication – ensure that on a daily basis either via formal or informal means, a check is made to ensure no changes are necessary to accommodate new patients admitted to the ward or patient movement around the ward.

In this case, significant improvements could be immediately made to benefit both the patient and the nursing staff simply by working smarter.

# TIP #85 IS CONTENT THE NEW HAPPY?

## ...ditch the clutter!

I believe that one's hospital stay should be made as happy as possible. We all face minor and major challenges throughout our life time and how we deal with them can be a strong indicator of how quickly we work through them, to know that the good times will once again roll.

A positive outlook on life will create positive things to happen and will help to reduce stress when our lives are not going so well.

One aspect that has a positive impact on our energy levels and well-being is the amount of items and personal belongings that we store around us which we do not use and from which we gain little sense of joy and appreciation.

One of my mother's life lessons was to "Get rid of anything that is not useful, beautiful or joyful".

When visiting check the bedside cabinets to make sure there are no old bits of food that need thrown out; read magazines with crosswords already completed; dirty washing that needs to be taken home and cleaned.

The clearing away of objects and foodstuffs that are no longer required will provide a calmer, cleaner environment that will be more welcoming for future visitors and more restful for the patient who has to live in these surroundings.

If you close the door on the rubbish, then you create new space for new things.

# TIP #86 MIND THAT YOU MATTER

## ...listen up!

How many of us on a regular or daily basis even when we are not in hospital really take the time to know and understand our friends and loved ones better? We often declare ourselves masters of small talk or talking about the football and latest television programmes, yet we do not truly make the time to properly talk and listen to one another.

Remember that an hour's visiting time can make all the difference to the in-patient. Seek to be present in the moment and not be worrying yourself about what you have or haven't done and what you are going to be doing. Slow down! If you are a person of few words then make them count. Listen to what your loved one or friend has to say to you. Know that they matter and make them feel that they matter and that you are not wishing you were somewhere else because the effort you have made to see them has made you run late for some other activity. I suggest sharing quality time and play your part to make them feel comfortable and confident. These actions will help their healing process and cannot be provided by hospital staff who are busy with their own work schedules. You may be surprised at how good you will feel too!

# TIP #87 LOCKED OUT!

## ...can you let me in?

Sometimes an in-patient does so well in their progress or the nature of their ailment is such that they are not confined to a bed and they are able to get dressed and take a walk around the hospital. When this happens, however, there can be an occasional issue. There was an incident when a lady who often chatted to my mother had taken a walk out into the hospital grounds without informing anyone of her whereabouts. When I arrived the following day to see Mum, she was standing just outside the main door to the hospital and she told me that the prior evening she had been accidentally locked out of the hospital because the main doors operated on an automated system after a certain time for the health and safety of the in-patients that were inside the hospital. Unfortunately when she had gone outside for a quiet smoke this night system had kicked in and she could not re-enter by the main doors. Instead, she had had to make her way down a steep grass area and enter back into the hospital via the Accident and Emergency entrance! She had found this a very frightening experience and one which she had no intention of repeating. Take good care and be watchful of others who look lost on your way out of hospital!

I think each of us knows that patient progress and measuring progress matters. Sometimes we expect progress to happen over a shorter time frame. One of the greatest gifts that I learned when I was visiting my Mum in hospital was to learn to be more compassionate and patient. When you offer compassion and patience to your friend and loved one then this helps them deal with the progress that is expected of them under the guidance of the medical staff. Knowing that you have helped your friend or loved one with the non-medical in-patient progress aspects means that you can feel valued from spending time with them and they in turn can feel more valued from the time spent in your company. Win, win! This is a great example in raising self-esteem for all concerned.

All of these elements impact on the recovery process and as improvement is made then the necessary exercise can start. In Chapter 9 Exercise which follows, I take a look at tips covering various exercises. The extent to which these are required, of course, is unique to each individual's circumstances and their own recovery plan implemented by the hospital.

# CHAPTER 9

## Exercise

When I was at school physical exercise was mandatory and I never gave it a second thought. As a result, I still enjoy various forms of exercise and do not view it as a burdensome task. I appreciate that this is not the case for everyone. Today, a person's lifestyle can dictate the amount of time, effort and energy they expend in this area. For a friend or loved one in hospital there may be specific requirements to undertake certain forms of exercise. If this is physical exercise as opposed to mental exercise, then physiotherapists will probably be scheduled to come in and work with the in-patient outside of visiting hours when possible. The tips in this chapter underline how important the visiting role is in providing support to the exercise routine.

# TIP #88 LET'S GET THE PHYSIO

## ...what a pain in the neck!

No matter how one is feeling, whether chirpy or a little low in spirit (not of the alcoholic variety, you understand – although for some the lack of this otherwise regular pleasure would exacerbate the depressed feelings!), it is necessary to listen to the physiotherapist in hospital when they tell you that some exercise is required. It is the easiest option to put off physiotherapy treatments until another day, but whatever specialist physiotherapy that is required, whether it includes soft tissue massage, mobilisation, manipulation or perhaps even hydrotherapy, acupuncture or even a combination of some or all of these, if the physiotherapist has established that a specific treatment is appropriate to help you, then it is a good idea to help yourself to wholeheartedly participate to benefit from the relief that it will bring you.

Lots of patience will be required both from the physiotherapist and the patient. I have seen several physiotherapists undertake their work with patients, and physiotherapy can be a very slow process. It can also be, however, a very rewarding process for both patient and physiotherapist when progress is made. I have a dear friend who, after an accident was left paralysed for two and a half years before a nurse noticed the smallest of movements in the pinkie finger of one of their hands. At that time, she then started lengthy physiotherapy treatment and the person now has the freedom of a normal life once again and undertakes sixty press-ups every day to maintain good health and avoid back and neck pains.

There should be no urgency or hurrying in physiotherapy treatments at any stage. Each person is unique in their requirements. Sessions with physiotherapists will vary between

15 minutes and a few hours, depending on the severity of the problems or disorders.

From my observations in hospitals, I have evidenced how physiotherapy can bring relief and improvement to a variety of patients who have suffered the loss of movement, impaired mobility, weakness of limbs and stiffness of the body, as examples.

A speedy recovery may be the luxury of the few, but determination and a strong will to concentrate on improvement will do the trick! Physiotherapy is for all ages and no-one should strain themselves beyond their physical capacity.

As visitors, we can encourage the patient to practise any exercises they have been given under the appropriate supervision and give words of support and confidence to the patient, giving them hope of steady improvement.

# TIP #89 WALKIES WITH THE LAMPSHADE!

## ...step in time!

While physical exercise as part of everyone's routine is important in overall health and wellness, offering a variety of benefits including boosting one's immune system, helping to promote or maintain positive self-esteem and helping to prevent depression, the ingenuity of some individuals observed in hospital to find a way to walk required a delicate balance of drive, willpower and structure. I learned that providing pleasurable rewards can amazingly create eager and determined individuals!

I am by no means an intellectual expert on health, but I do find it both fascinating and amusing at the motivating factors that drive an individual to achieve their goals.

My mother had recently been transferred to a different ward and one of the patients with whom she was sharing this four bed ward, was of middle age and hooked up to a drip. The drip bag was attached to a pole equipped with a mobile base and the ability to adjust the height was able to be performed with one-hand if necessary. It was the use that this stand afforded the patient as a mode of sustainable transport that was of interest to this particularly astute lady. She clearly perceived new issues as new challenges, not as obstacles and was about to transform her latest bedside "obstacle" into her new travel companion. It did not matter to her whether the IV-pole was made of stainless steel, chrome steel or aluminium. What did matter was that it had a set of castors on the bottom and was easy and quick to use. It assisted her to self –sufficiently walk out of the ward to the front door of the hospital where she could indulge in her pleasure – a long awaited for cigarette. Have stand will travel!

This is surely testament that exercise is enjoyable when it does not feel like a struggle and to those of such inclination, that there is hope for a smoke!

# TIP #90 STAND TO ATTENTION

## ...with an 'aid' memoire!

The wonder of medical care in hospitals today is that there are useful aids available to ease the mobility of a patient. These are not necessarily available in the home environment. For all carers in the community, I would urge you to take note in case this is one piece of equipment that would help you with your care member.

My mother required help to transfer between the bed, the chair and the toilet. There was a brilliant standing hoist with easy manoeuvrability that she was able to use designed for standing, sitting, dressing and toileting.

There were leg supports that could be adjusted and these were positioned to mirror the natural motion of a patient for comfort. The frame was designed to reduce the risk of awkward twisting, a factor which was also relevant to my mother who had had a hip replacement some ten years ago. The equipment was designed to allow close placement to the wheelchair, chair or toilet. This removed the need for manual handling when moving the user back into the seated position. The patient is able to stand with support for knees, hips and torso. The standing aid also has powered opening and closing legs, to assist where space is at a premium.

The additional benefit of using a standing aid is that standing with suitable support strengthens muscles and joints. If muscles are unused for as little as 24 hours then they can start to lose tone.

# TIP #91 TAKE A WALK ON THE BRIGHT SIDE

## ...best foot forward outside!

Air is one of the few commodities for which we do not pay! Is it really a tradable commodity? I would answer yes to this question if it is asked when addressed in the context of the confines of a hospital.

How many times have you walked out of your house or office and never given it a second thought? The fact is that when one is in hospital, the seemingly free enjoyment of fresh air is no longer able to be taken for granted. Sometimes at best there is a ward room window that can be opened. I have experienced a problem when there was a window in the ward but it was faulty and for a time could not even be opened; most unhygienic not to mention health and safety implications!

Anyway, one way to provide a change of environment from the ward is to offer to walk with your friend or relative into the hospital grounds for some fresh air. This can be a real tonic and is also providing exercise too!

If, like my mother, the patient requires the assistance of a wheelchair then this can be collected on the entrance to the hospital, where there is usually a holding area for these chairs. When they are in high demand and short supply then I would suggest walking to the lift areas where there are often abandoned wheelchairs. On the way if you pass a porter, then politely stop him and ask if the empty wheelchair he is pushing is needed elsewhere or if you can have it. There are usually never enough spare wheelchairs at visiting times to meet the demand.

Check out the hospital grounds on arrival and find out where there are relaxation areas for patients. Be careful as some areas are made with crazy paving stones that have worn and can be very uneven. Take extra care when walking across these areas with a wheelchair.

In milder weather think about the enjoyment of having a drink of tea or coffee out in the fresh air, rather than sitting inside in the ward among other patients. The energy boost from a change of scene will help boost the immune system and general well-being of the patient. In cooler, drier weather bring a lightweight rug to slip over the person's legs to keep them warm. Remember that they will be more susceptible to a change in temperature if they have been in a hospital ward for some time.

During the summer months I would endeavour to take Mum out of the ward into the fresher air every day. Sometimes I also took up small tubs of wonderful white Italian ice cream with raspberry sauce that we would eat in the hospital gardens. By the end of the summer my mother had quite a sun-tan on her hands, face and forearms and looked really well.

# TIP #92 PROMENADE PARKING

## ...Excuse me, Mrs. Motivator!

Strolls and leisurely walks inside the hospital and around the hospital grounds as often as possible should be encouraged. The engagement of such an activity can be a great solution to taking daily exercise and if shared in good company, it can be most pleasurable, without feeling like a mandatory chore.

The pathways and corridors of the hospitals require careful traffic management skills and manoeuvrability manners as they are places of constant congestion with obstacles galore!

It took me a few days to work out how to successfully use the different wheelchair functions effectively and to work out distances passing through doorways. Most people are very considerate when they see you and kindly keep doors open to let you pass through. These kindnesses can quickly dispel any sense of frustration that builds up as you negotiate your way around the strange trails seeking fresh air and freedom.

Remember that once outside in the hospital grounds having found a favourite area to stop, that wheelchair brakes should be applied for safety and ideally you should choose a place that will not hinder oncoming traffic. If your family member or friend requires the assistance of a "Motivator" or Zimmer frame for confidence in walking, then once you are comfortably seated, this should be carefully positioned so that no-one else passing by you will trip up over it.

Another tip that I learned about using the wheelchairs made available in the hospital is that as the driver, it is often easier to pull them along the corridors to one's destination rather than push them. This is typical of the models without handles. And yes, it does mean that the person in the wheelchair is seated facing out in the direction from which they have been pulled, but it makes for a much smoother ride.

When you are taking a break for a drink or just resting outside always remember to apply the brakes on either side of the wheelchair to avoid any further accidental damage. Otherwise you could be off on an impromptu adventure!

As the reader of this tips book having finished Chapter 9 Exercise, are you out of breath yet? I hope this mental exercise will not deter you from making time to fit in, excuse the pun, some time for your own physical exercise too! Both an in-patient and their visitor(s) need to keep themselves as healthy as possible and often the timetable of scheduling in visiting can be difficult to the extent that visitors forget to look after their own health. Just when you thought it must be the end I have twelve further tips for you to explore in Chapter 10 Miscellany.

# CHAPTER 10

## Miscellany

What else is there to think about? After writing the last nine chapters of tips covering admission to hospital and including the in-patient's primary needs like hygiene and then considering secondary needs such as entertainment, I surprised myself that there were still twelve tips left over which I have categorised under the title Miscellany; not long until Going Home. Enjoy!

# TIP #93 MIND THE BUZZ...ER!

## ...time is of the essence!

Visiting times on the wards and throughout hospitals change periodically and are set differently. Generally one will not be allowed onto a ward outside of visiting times other than in the most exceptional circumstances. Hospital wards are extremely busy areas and certainly as a standard rule there is no visiting permitted during protected meal times, to enable patients to eat without interruption.

I can understand this discipline and practice. The handheld controllers attached to long cords plugged into each patient bed-side are designed to help ease any possible patient hypertension. The reassurance should come from knowing that when help is required it is only the press of a buzzer away. In theory this sounds like the perfect solution to patient care, especially when visitors are not around to be the second voice or an extra pair of hands to address a patient's needs. In practice, however, the opportunity for the patient to use it can be overlooked by both hospital staff and visitors. What if that vital aid to help and reassurance is missing or out of eye-shot?

There is no use for a unit to boast a new hand-held buzzer system alerting patients to summon help, if the buzzer is not within reach of the patient to use!

The different situations I have encountered with my own mother's hospital stays have been as follows:

- Buzzer plug disconnected from the wall;
- Buzzer not working and therefore in need of repair;
- Buzzer left on bedside cabinet out of reach of both my mother's peripheral vision and her physical reach.

The buzzer is an essential piece of equipment that provides additional assurance and help to a patient. This is especially so when a patient has impaired mobility and / or when they have no use of their vocal chords to speak.

Many patients also need assistance to go to the toilet. I have heard that ladies are more prone to urinary tract infections that men. One of my medical friends told me that this may be because bacteria can reach the bladder in a female quicker than a male due to the female having a shorter urethra. I'll take their word for it!

Regardless of the medical facts, my mother always told me, "Don't delay going to the bathroom when you need to. It is bad for your kidneys to hold in waste." Sometimes even after having pressed her buzzer to request a commode, she would wait eight minutes before someone would appear to help her. Frequently during visiting times, by the time the nurse turned up at her side, she had lost the urge to go the toilet and she would send the commode back!

An additional factor that I observed mainly with the more mature generation of patient in a ward, was that they were often less likely to buzz for help than their more youthful counterparts, for fear of "being a burden" or "being a nuisance" to the nursing staff. When a patient is statistically less likely to buzz for help, this is all the more reason to ensure that when they do consider it really urgent, that they do have access to use the buzzer. How sanitary are the buzzers given to patients in hospitals?

Buzzers are very useful and necessary to indicate to a staff member that help is required. I have not seen how these are sanitised, however, and the frequency with which this would be done, and so while they do not wholly allay my fears of viruses and bacteria being spread, the practical need for use of these by patients far outweighs any bacterium threat!

Remember that broken buzzers and inaccessible buzzers can strand hospital patients and impede their healing!

I would always be aware of other patients in the ward who pressed their buzzer for assistance during visiting time and for those patients who needed to press a buzzer, but whose buzzer was out of their reach. Just a little thought to observe what else is going on around your family member or friend being visited could really help out someone else and it only takes a second! On another occasion it may be your loved one that appreciates the help from a stranger!

# TIP #94 BROTHER, CAN YOU SPARE A DIME

## ...a euro, a penny?

Whenever I thought that Mum would not necessarily want a drink at afternoon visiting or I was simply in too much of a rush to reach the hospital on time for the start of visiting having previously made up a flask of hot water etc., I would inevitably get caught out with a lack of change to buy two coffees or two teas!

The reality is that two teas in the main canteen were significantly cheaper than two teas purchased at the more fashionable coffee shop nearer the elevator leading up to Mum's ward. Either way, however, when one does not even have 99p to buy the less expensive tea option from loose change carried in one's purse then lateral thinking comes into play. I cannot put 99p on my credit card, nor would I if I could, because the administration fee for so doing would probably cost me another £5 on top of the 99p and that would be an expensive cup of tea for two! When I walked all the way back down the corridor to the far end of the courtyard reception I did notice a queue at the cash point. One lady turned round to me in the queue and explained that the cash machine would not release £20 notes. Oh no! Perhaps, though, it would release £10 notes. Ahhh! Success! Only now, fifteen minutes into precious visiting time am I now in a position to run back down the long corridor to buy the tea at 99p! Meantime, Mum is upstairs in her ward wondering what has kept me and where her tea is, feeling slighted that she has had time stolen from her with me that she will never get back! I am still on a marathon run, remembering to ask for a cup cover to make sure I do not burn my hands carrying the hot cups up to the ward! The last thing I need now is for some young child to stop me on the way back to the ward and ask me for a penny for the Guy! The moral of the story is that one should always carry an emergency supply of change to ensure one can at the very least afford to buy two cups of hot drinks and a biscuit at visiting time.

Thankfully most visitors are often in the mood for sharing a little kindness and I have been helped out with two pence on another occasion when I was short of change for drinks. Equally, I have paid this forward by helping out a complete stranger who like me was caught out too!

Oh yes, and one thing I would recommend in relation to purchasing any hot drinks would be to use the cardboard cup sleeve holders to avoid burning one's hands!

# TIP #95 BARTERERS WHO SHARE

## ...the Big Apple!

I never realised that there are so many things to consider when you know of someone that is a patient in hospital. It is not always suitable to leave money with a patient. They may be nervous about having a purse left either out in the open on top of their bedside cabinet or even tucked inside a drawer. As luck would have it, whenever I chose to leave Mum without a few pennies, that would be the time when the hostess came round with the trolley of magazines and snacks and of course when my mother would feel like a drink or a piece of chocolate. On a couple of occasions, at least one of the other patients with whom she was sharing the ward, would come up trumps and lend the money to Mum to enable her to buy the drink or confectionery item. As soon as I appeared at visiting time, Mum would hasten me to repay the lady after which she then felt she could relax again. My mother was always taught, neither a borrower nor a lender be, and took this very seriously.

In addition to this generosity, however, there was always plenty of gifted fruit, biscuits and chocolates to go around. I used to take in sweets and biscuits for the nursing staff on the ward too, and often patients would swap a biscuit for a piece of fruit and vice versa. It was great to evidence a group of strangers coming together under stressful circumstances yet helping one another out! So next time you take a gift in to your friend or relative, remember a little extra to "go around" the ward too!

# TIP #96 I'LL TRADE A TISSUE

## ...bless you!

Although I have observed most visitors to be very generous with their gifts, the thought of taking in a more practical box of tissues over a beautiful bouquet of flowers or a hamper of fresh fruit, never usually crosses one's mind.

As previously mentioned there is as a rule, at least one shop in each hospital that carries the basic supplies should patients be caught out with toiletries, but there is also a premium price to be paid for these products.

Once in a while it is necessary to think about more practical gifts that will be as warmly received as others simply because they remove the worry and anxiety from the patient of now having these basics.

# TIP #97 FAULTY SHOWERS!

## ...a little unhinged!

Bathing time, although often a rarity in hospitals, should be a time for relaxation, freshness and promoting a sense of well-being! When a patient has impaired mobility then the chance to have a bath or a shower can be most gratifying.

Whether one is young or old, disabled or disfigured, the joy of bathtime should be a real treat! And nowadays hospitals provide wet rooms, easy access showers and full length baths to accommodate each person's cleansing needs.

What should have been a suitable showering solution, on one occasion, ended up being a significant slip-up when one of my friends as a patient in a private hospital for a knee replacement was left alone in the shower. Some shower doors are folding doors. These shower doors were hinged doors. When my friend stepped out of the shower, the door became unhinged! Oops! She was lucky it did not fall on her and cause an injury! By all means be relaxed at bath-time but don't go head over heels!

# TIP #98 WHAT THE BEEP...?

## ...sound advice on saving Grace!

Wards are traditionally noisy places. Whether it is the clatter of trolleys or the chatter of hospital staff, noise is always in the background. There are always staff members coming and going, changing drips, checking patients' blood pressure, transferring patients, porters taking them for x-rays and other tests, physiotherapists offering words of encouragement to patients in need of exercise and this is all outwith the hectic hours of visiting times.

One point that I made earlier was that each patient has a handheld buzzer to attract the attention of a ward staff member. This is not always available within the patient's reach and therefore I would suggest that you are extra vigilant to the sounds that you hear around you when you are visiting.

Previously unfamiliar with hospitals, despite a stint on hospital radio back in the1990's, I did not know what the many noises meant. There are quite distinct sounds made, however, when a drip is fitted to a patient. When the IV (intravenous) solution has emptied then a different sound resonates indicating that the machine either needs to be switched off or the medicinal bag needs to be changed for a new one. Noises can be very disturbing and disruptive both to a patient and to visitors. In many cases there is nothing to worry about, but in others it can be related to a health problem.

When assessing whether the noises you are hearing present a concern, consider its impact on the patient, you and the other visitors and patients around you. Is the noise particularly loud? Is the noise causing distress to the patient or on the ward? Consider whether it is appropriate to take the practical steps of either buzzing for a nursing staff member to alert their attention to this or getting up yourself and going to the central station to report the incident. You could help save a life! Remember to leave all other buttons, buzzers and bags to the professional staff.

# TIP #99 SHOP AND COLIC?

## ...have your pin money!

Make sure that you always have a little change with you in your wallet or purse for unplanned incidentals that you can purchase from the hospital shop. This will prevent you from becoming very frustrated.

I would always try to remember everything to take into Mum at visiting time but it was not unusual for me to pop down to the voluntarily manned hospital shop to buy a few magazines or to buy a packet of sandwiches for Mum because she was feeling particularly hungry that day.

These shops will vary in size from hospital to hospital. The larger hospitals will carry a good supply of newspapers, magazines, sandwiches, sweets, soft drinks, batteries, tissues, toothbrushes, cards, flowers and ice cream. Just what one needs if one is running behind schedule!

It's a good idea to carry some loose change because they seldom carry a large stock of change themselves and not all hospitals have a cash machine in the grounds if you are short of money.

# TIP #100 SHE'S ALWAYS A WOMAN

## ...access all areas!

I included this section as it was merely an observation that the wards in which my mother inhabited were either single sex wards or else very carefully arranged to house both males and females within their own sections of multi-bed areas.

As my mother was of an older generation, there was an expectation that the wards would be of the same sex. This privacy afforded her a certain amount of dignity and respect that would have been diluted should she have been in a mixed bedded area.

I have to agree that if I was unwell I would prefer to have the segregation of males from females too. It would be bad enough being in a ward with other patients to start with, having everyone see you when you were not feeling your best.

# TIP #101 PARKING MANIA

## ...round the bend!

Finding a parking space in hospital grounds can be a real challenge! Given the anxiousness of your friend or loved one in hospital, the last thing you want to worry about is finding a space for your car! I was at a loss to understand why when I visited during the day before 5pm, the hospital car parks were nearly always full. Naïvely I had assumed that the majority of individuals employed still work between 8am and 6pm and so theoretically, the car parks should be almost empty. Not so! I had not planned on day clinics taking place at the hospital. These would last until at least 3pm and visiting at various hospitals commenced either at 2.30pm or 3pm – an overlap on one of the peak parking times for the daily hospital visits!

Where the hospital is located will depend on whether parking charges are in force. Not all meters for charges will provide change and so it is best to make sure you carry a few coins with you at all times to avoid further frustration and disappointment.

If you are naturally a person who leaves doing something until the last minute, then hospital visiting will force you to change your ways unless you want to lose out on valuable visiting time.

Suggestions for making the parking process easier are to plan your visit to the hospital twenty minutes before the start of visiting time. In this way, if you cannot find a parking space in the grounds of the hospital, there is a good chance you will find a space outside this area and still have time to walk to the ward without missing out on personal time.

Twenty minutes might give the impression of too much time, but if you also have to find a wheelchair, buy a cup of coffee in the canteen, purchase a magazine and some sweets in the hospital shop before you have reached the ward to say, "Hello!", then your time will very quickly disappear!

# TIP #102 OBSERVATION

## ...no stimulation!

Few of us really take the time to observe other people and their behaviour. We are all too busy rushing around meeting deadlines that we have imposed on ourselves and sometimes there is a little bit of the martyr in each of us that enjoys the rush, and considers that although we say we would give anything to have a quiet weekend in, would we really be lost with what to do without our hectic schedules? Go figure?

Well, for sadder reasons (the ill health of my mother), I chose to take a step back from full time corporate work and use that newly released time to spend more time with Mum while she was unwell. As I was visiting her at least twice each day, I would notice many things. In particular, I noticed that with many patients, and especially the more mature patients, they would often close their eyes pretending to be asleep or indulging in an afternoon siesta! Having experienced a little of their world in what is for most, a completely unstimulated environment it was no wonder that many patients chose to close their eyes and shut out the pain of their clinical and fearful surroundings together with their unstimulated muscles!

Obviously there were genuine periods when sleep would take over the adult, but from the twitching and non-verbal body language that occurred, I could tell that much of it was feigned. To give a false appearance of sleeping may delay daily exercise, which in the long term was probably doing them no favours. Moreover, it made me realise that in the general wards one really had no privacy. There was a distinct lack of stimulus to heal and get well again!

# TIP #103 LOST IN TRANSIT

## ...the Crown Jewels!

Following the transfer of my mother at around 3.05am one morning from one ward to another within the same hospital, I noticed when I visited her that afternoon at 3pm that my mother's long gold chain was missing from around her neck. She stated to me that she had felt for it earlier in the day but could not feel it. She only had a shorter gold chain still around her neck at this time.

This lost three-tone gold metal necklace was of great sentimental value to my mother because it was a gift from me back in 1992. Fortunately, I had several photographs of Mum wearing this necklace as she had only ever taken it off for a few hospital scans since I gave it to her. I ensured a photo was supplied for scanning into the hospital system in the hope that the necklace would be recovered together with my letter of complaint.

From speaking to several jewellers in the local area, all of them stated that jewellery going missing in hospitals was a regular occurrence! Having worked at Cartier myself I was very familiar with the robust nature of a lobster claw clasp. The clasp that was on my mother's chain was a reinforced lobster-claw lock and once on, it is extremely unlikely to come undone or break. As the jewellery had been recently checked for safety I found this incident very uncomfortable. Moreover, my mother then felt even more fearful of staying in hospital wondering what would happen to her next.

At this point it is appropriate to mention the alleged "get out" clause that NHS hospitals have by way of a caveat to all personal property. It reads something like this:

The hospital cannot accept liability for money or valuables brought onto its premises unless they are hand in for safe-keeping and a receipt obtained.

Would someone like to inform me please how they expect an 85 years young person whose sleep is disturbed in the middle of the night and who has been classed as "very vulnerable" to ask for her personal property to be handed in for safe keeping and to check that she obtains a receipt for this, before she is without notice, moved to another ward? This practice is unacceptable!

I naturally raised this as a complaint issue of lost jewellery with the administration office. They informed me that I would be required to write a letter explaining the lost property incident and nature of the jewellery lost and to address it generally for the attention of someone in the General Office. Meantime, a formal Claim Form would be sent down to the ward from the administration department for the staff to fill in and record the incident.

Now the practices of each hospital probably do not differ significantly across each hospital and I would urge you to make the time to lodge the lost jewellery as a formal written complaint should this unfortunate experience happen to you.

Why? Well, each complaint has to be formally recognised by the Hospital Board and explanations obtained for the complaint and a review of the satisfactory dealing of each complaint. The only way that improvements can be made is if the Board knows what is going on.

It took me three days of asking the staff at the central station for a claim form without success before I asked if I could help them out by going to the general administration office to obtain one myself. It was only when I did this (during visiting hours and therefore to the distinct dissatisfaction of my mother) that I was then told the ward staff have to fill out the claim form which is not for my viewing and I needed to write my own letter to the general office to formally lodge the incident! Let's just bear in mind at this point, that my mother's health is far more important than a lost item of jewellery but on a point of principle if my mother, who was identified by the medical staff as "very vulnerable", is going to be in the habit of being moved without me being informed in the middle of the night and some of her jewellery mysteriously goes missing then I want the fact recorded for the Board!

Remember that one has to have an official Claim Reference Number from the hospital in order that one can notify the insurance company of the property lost.

I have listed the points that one should consider to describe any lost jewellery as follows:

- Description of Lost Jewellery
- Metal:
- Design Type:
- Material Type:
- Length: in approx. centimetres or inches, denoting which measurement was used
- Width: in approx. millimetres
- Total Metal Weight: in Approx. grammes.

As soon as you realise that you have personal property missing ask for a complaints brochure and if you are not able, then ask someone who is, to help you lodge your complaint in writing.

Consider checking out the following places as soon as possible:

- check under the bedcovers;
- down the sides of the bed;
- down the sides of the chair that you have been using;
- check under tables, beds and chairs in case the item has rolled or accidentally been kicked across the floor;
- check the wash room and toilet areas;
- check tissue boxes and glasses cases;
- ask for the ward safe to be checked in case another person has handed it in for safe keeping.

The price of all metals has recently increased substantially and so make sure that if the piece is quite old that you find out the equivalent current market value from a reliable source.

For those of you who consider I may have been irresponsible in leaving my mother wearing her two necklace chains, I have the following comment to make. Other than when she had a few hospital scans, my mother always wore these pieces of jewellery, even to bed and in the bath and shower. She had been happily wearing both pieces since 1992. When one is in hospital it is a little more dignified and comfortable to do the things you would normally do at home, without depersonalising the individual altogether. Had my mother selectively worn these pieces of jewellery I would never have left them on her, but they had become an integral part of her. The fact that she was moved in the middle of the night gives me cause for concern in other areas too.

Exactly what are the Patient Statistics across hospitals on the number of patients that are moved in the middle of the night? Is this routine? Is this key performance indicator even measured?

Was there not a duty of care to my mother as an eighty five year old lady who was elderly, unwell, suffered from occasional confusion and was already anxious about her circumstances?

My understanding is that Standards of Practice require that NMAHPs must provide high quality care across "the whole journey of care" and that a patient should feel safe and be safe. I do not consider that the transfer of an elderly patient at this time (3.05am) is met with "receiving kindness" and with the minimum practice standards of respect of the patient by the "NMAHPs who must be alert to vulnerability, acting always in the most appropriate manner to meet needs".

After all of this, do not be put off taking in pieces of jewellery, costume or fine, and allowing your friend or loved-one to at least wear the piece(s) during visiting times to make them feel loved and human.

# TIP # 104 REMEMBER YOUR T'S AND Q'S

## ...organised chaos!

Throughout the caring process each of us is pushed to our limit at some point. It is especially at this time that is it important to stop yourself and take a deep breath. I have always found even when you are feeling anxious, frustrated or out of your depth and comfort zone due to a lack of knowledge, that the best way to work through this is always to treat others with respect. This means remember those important words, "thank you" and to ask a question when you are unsure.

There is no such thing as a stupid question or indeed a difficult or easy question. It is a matter of fact. You either know the answer or you don't, in which case don't be afraid to ask for some help.

As an unofficial carer for my mother myself, I was always a very private person about my mother's needs and was reluctant to ask for help until very late on. I think there was also an aspect of me that told me inside my head that if I didn't talk about it then perhaps the issue was not as profound as it really was.

Are we there yet? Yes, almost. Congratulate yourself on reaching the end of Chapter 10 Miscellany, where all those other tips had their place. Now you can begin to relax a little more yourself and reduce those stress levels because it is finally time for your loved-one to go home. The final chapter, Chapter 11 Going Home, addresses those tips to help you out of the door of the hospital safely. Onwards, upwards and outwards!

# CHAPTER 11

## Going Home

Isn't going home from anything a wonderful feeling, be it a holiday, an event, social gathering, special occasion or in this case a return home from a stay in hospital? Chapter 11 focuses on those aspects that will need to be checked off before your friend or loved-one can finally walk out through the hospital doors.

One of my friends mentioned about the importance of life after visiting a loved one in hospital and feeling the void if a loved one has passed on. Sadly in some cases a loved one or friend passes on or dies in hospital. Going Home for some individuals, therefore, may be a call to go home at a deeper level than the physical action of being collected and taken in a car or ambulance back to one's physical home. In this case it is a return to source and a passing on from this physical world through death. Thankfully my mother's last breath breathed was very peaceful and serene. The time that I had chosen to spend with her left me guilt free and privileged to have had the opportunity to spend so much time with such a loving person who had only ever had my own best interests at heart. Now it is my turn to touch your heart and the ones you love and to encourage you to "feel the love" and help your loved one or friend to improve their healing experience in hospital and on their return to home.

# TIP #105 HOLD THE DREAM

## ...hope of release!

Hope is that wonderful feeling that what you would like to turn out will happen. This feeling is great to have especially if you find that your stay in hospital is longer term than you had first anticipated or, for example, that it is suggested that you require more tests to be undertaken to establish the cause and cure of your dis-ease.

My mother was always full of hope and frequently held a vision in her own mind that saw her steadfast through the challenges in her life.

I think that I too have her strength of hope and came across a beautiful Swedish quote that I would like you to read and enjoy:

*"Fear less, hope more;*

*Eat less, chew more;*

*Whine less, breathe more;*

*Talk less, say more;*

*Love more, and all good things will be yours"*

# TIP #106 TAKE IT AWAY

## ...luggage for leaving!

Luggage trunks, backpacks, vanity cases, garment carriers, traditional suitcases – just a few methods for transporting our personal belongings!

When it is time to be discharged from hospital there is seldom much notice given to the patient. If your loved one was originally admitted to hospital as an emergency case, there is a high probability that few personal belongings were brought in with them at that time. Since their stay in hospital, however, there is a good chance that their personal belongings have expanded with the good wishes and gifts of well-wishers and requirements to bring in day clothes as part of a rehabilitation programme. This change in circumstances will dictate the need for some form of luggage to be made available to the patient for the safe carriage home of their valuables and personal items.

The distance the person will require to travel and their mode of transport will determine suitability of luggage used. If the individual is going to be accompanied, then consideration of the ability of the person to be able to carry bags is an issue and especially when they are travelling alone. Even if someone of good health is going to be escorting them, however, and public transport will be used, then a proper bag that is more robust than a thin, plastic carrier bag whose handles may burst under excess weight, is preferable.

Innovative solutions are now available including ultra lightweight luggage on wheels that make carriage easy for either the patient or their companion. These products are both functional and stylish.

# TIP #107 NEW HOME

## ...a new outlook on life!

While it is everyone's hope that they are allowed to return to their own home when they are discharged from hospital, sometimes the in-patient's condition requires consideration of longer term care out of hospital in the form of a residential care home, nursing home or perhaps a retirement home.

If consideration of a move to a new home is necessary to facilitate the extra care that is needed to enable the in-patient to be discharged from hospital, then it is important that you do your best for them and consider what their likes and dislikes are and how these preferences for various activities, hobbies and interests can be matched with the choice of new home offered.

Many of the residential care homes offer frequent bus trips on the care home's own private bus and also have an in-house hair salon and beauty room or at the very least have a mobile hairdresser to visit. All these different activities can help to ease your friend and loved one into a new lifestyle and encourage them to make new friends.

There has been much scrutiny surrounding care homes over the last five years. There is now a new inspection rating system implemented by the Quality Care Commission that assesses various criteria and gives an overall rating which will be one of the following:

- Outstanding
- Good
- Requires Improvement
- Inadequate

My suggestion to you would be to filter the care homes in the respective area and focus on finding availability at those identified as 'outstanding'. Why would you want anything less than the best for your friend or loved one? Take a note of where these are and phone up and go and visit them. Undertake your own assessment of the care home. Include in your assessment the telephone response that you receive when you first contact them and the welcome that you receive when you arrive and how long they spend to show you around and whether they allow you to speak to any of the current residents. This will all help to give you a feel of whether you could imagine your friend or loved one living there. If it is possible, ask for a visit for your friend or loved one prior to them making a decision on their care home. Some care homes look great on the website or brochure but the real test is to experience the warmth of welcome and the feeling that you have when you physically visit the home. How does the care home interact with the rest of the local community? For example, do they invite musicians, singers, dancers and other artists into their premises to hold concerts for the residents?

Remember the more often that each of us finding ourselves in this position takes the time to do this and ask questions, then the greater the probability and possibility of improving the overall standard of care in the home. Each one of us acting in this way benefits all residents and seeks to give peace of mind to the rest of the family that loved ones are well looked after.

# TIP #108 A ROOM WITH A VIEW

## ...and window sill!

When it is time to return home but mobility of the individual may be restricted, consider arranging a room in their home which allows them to be able to sit comfortably at a window, especially if they are likely to spend quite a lot of time recuperating. In this way, they will become less bored and feel more of a connection with the community again.

Where your friend or loved one is going to spend time in a residential care home because they are no longer able to live independently they may have their own room rather than a full house to themselves. In this case think about the size and brightness of the room and the facilities that are both in the room itself and those generally throughout the care home. Think about how similar the environment and room layout is to their former home situation and if you know that they were happy, then seek to mirror this again. You may be involved in helping them make the final decision and so it is important to seek to understand what they specifically like and what type of environment would make them happy and content. For example, my mother loved animals, nature and especially trees. It was important for me to find a room for her that looked out on to beautiful trees and woodland so that she could both see the countryside from her window and also hear the birds singing. If this is not an option then perhaps there is the possibility of having a planter box on the window sill to bring an element of nature closer to your friend and loved one.

# TIP #109 FULLY FUNCTIONAL

## ...a testing time!

It is to be hoped that the majority of in-patients will return home feeling fully recovered and back to their normal health. For a few, however, there will be a few changes that may require to be made. Some of these changes may be short term and for others there may be more physical changes made around the house to accommodate an easier life.

For example, when someone is returning from hospital with a plaster on their leg after a serious break it will be important to ensure that all access areas are free from clutter to avoid any further incident. If your loved-one has had injuries that impede mobility then perhaps a bed may need to be moved down from a bedroom upstairs to a sitting room located downstairs on a temporary basis, to improve the healing process and reduce worries about getting to and from different rooms in the house. There may need to be more permanent home improvement changes made to the bathroom and / or the staircase when an individual returns home and has longer term difficulties with walking. When there are outside stairs at the back or front of their house then a ramp can often make access easier. Sometimes this would also be supplemented with a handrail.

I found the best way to deal with these various issues was to think about one issue at a time and remain calm and positive throughout the change process, safe in the knowledge that everything that was being done for my Mum was for her benefit and improved quality of life. It was as much about me remaining optimistic and patient to have various aids installed throughout the work being done to keep my Mum feeling confident and positive too! It is so important to embrace the change and refuse to think of these changes as a burden to family members.

# TIP #110 HOME SWEET HOME

## ...a sigh of belief!

Every day when I visited my mother within about ten minutes of visiting she would always ask me when she was getting home. It really pained me to have to skirt around this issue so many times over the eight months that she was in hospital and be unable to give her a direct answer. I used to keep telling her that she was in the best possible place to address the health challenges that she had and that as soon as possible she would be able to return home. I would then change the conversation topic to avoid any further awkward questions about this.

I appreciate that for many of you, your loved one, friend or colleague may only be in hospital for a short period of time and you will be in a stronger position to know specifically when discharge will occur. Once this date has been given to you then I would encourage you to keep the in-patient's mind on a positive outcome and to buoy up their feelings and confidence level as they focus on this date. Hopefully, this will minimise the anxiety of the in-patient for the remainder of time that they spend in hospital in the run up to this release date.

# TIP #111 LOVE AND GRATITUDE

## ...perfect peace!

Lyrics to my song titled Perfect Peace

*When music sings its song of love and draws you to attention*
*Listen to the impact that it has on your affection*
*For the joy of life, that each day brings*
*Without the need for material things,*
*Should never be neglected,*
*But be cherished, honoured and protected.*
*So next time when you breathe in air*
*Breathe in hope and not despair,*
*Know that love will get you there*
*Live your life in peace.*

I do hope that having finished reading Chapter 11 Going Home, both your loved-ones as in-patients and visitors alike have found at least one tip in this book helpful in channelling any stress and negative emotions into a more pleasurable, healing experience.

# CONCLUSION

The suggested tips that I have collated for this book are only a starter for guidance on how to feel and express love to a fellow friend, acquaintance, relative, partner, lover, visitor, patient and staff member when visiting a hospital. I am sure that many of you who read or even partially "dip in" to this book will at the very least be able to relate to the importance that just a smile can make when one is not "up to par" and at best come up with your own tips!

Not only was it fun to collate all of these suggestions and distract me from my own life challenges, but it was empowering and encouraging to me to write with the intention that these tips are not confined to any time or space. Some of them are as relevant to everyday living whether one is at home, in the workplace, on holiday or even out for a walk. All of us can feel the love from a small comment made across a counter at a food store, for example, whether we are fully healthy or not. Our words and actions are, at an unconscious level, food for the soul. How many of you have felt a spring in your step because you were given a compliment on the way into work? On one occasion I was standing outside Birmingham airport waiting for a private taxi, when a chap in a four-wheel drive vehicle drove passed me, rolled down his window, leaned out and said, "You look lovely with that coat on!", smiled and drove on! I had a warm fuzzy feeling in my stomach for several hours afterwards and I was definitely more productive that morning because I felt really good about myself from that one comment.

Feeling the love brings benefits to all involved. The person who speaks their truth and sends a loving thought, smile, gesture or spoken word feels good about giving it and the receiver "feels the love". Often unknowingly this is passed on to other individuals who then come into contact with both parties, who, in turn, receive a compliment or kind word.

Love is infectious. Live your love and truly "FEEL THE LOVE"!

# ABOUT THE AUTHOR

Lady Wise delivers her work in a relaxed and entertaining style conducive to learning. Her approach is creative and flexible and she seeks to always be informal, friendly and humorous. By profession she is an internationally travelled financial and strategic consultant. For a short period prior to her beloved mother (and best friend) ascending, her own corporate world was put on temporary hold. She chose to take on the role of unofficial 'carer' without any medical experience whatsoever. Lady Wise decided to channel her positivity from this experience to write her first book in the hope that this would help others, especially the sandwich generation, going through similar life challenges.

It is her logical approach to the practical issues affecting those of us who find ourselves looking after a vulnerable loved-one who has suddenly been admitted into hospital, which provides a structure to the many issues that arise in this event. She seeks to deliver practical solutions to the many questions that one has when they find their whole world turned upside down when their loved-one is admitted to hospital.

Lady Wise wants to help your loved-one feel the love of HOME in hospital.

# OTHER BOOKS OF INTEREST

If you have enjoyed reading this Feel The Love 111 Tips Book, perhaps you may also be interested to know that Volume 2 is now available in paperback and as an ebook too, entitled, "Feel The Love 111 Tips When Caring For Someone at Home". This tips guide is to help deliver an improved healing and living experience. It is especially for those of you who have a friend or loved-one who is still living at home but who requires that extra attention of love and care from you to ensure that they have a great living experience!

After successfully publishing "Feel the Love" Volume 1 tips book, "When Visiting Someone in Hospital", many of you asked me to follow this up promptly with a tips book that focused on the subtle and additional variations that would be required when a friend or loved-one is at home on their own or indeed living with a relative, but who is in need of a little extra care.

Sometimes the realisation that a loved-one or friend is becoming a little less independent of their daily living is difficult to come to terms with physically, emotionally, mentally and spiritually. It can often be difficult to know how best to deal with this new situation especially if it appears to be disrupting what was always a regular routine for you. Can you even begin to imagine, therefore, how it must feel for your friend or loved-one when they are aware of their inhibited living ability and choose to be in denial about it because they are fighting their own independence? My mother in her late seventies at the time was exactly in this category and it required a very delicate and understanding approach to encourage her to 'slow down' and in some cases, undertake things from a different perspective in order to protect her from "doing herself a mischief!"

You want to do what is best both for you as the (often unpaid and untrained) "carer" and for your loved- one or friend in need of that care. You are keen to make sure that they have all they need during the time when you are NOT present as much as when you are there for them.

One of the first things you may notice as a 'carer' is how it "changes" your world and your daily routine. This, alone, may become very stressful as each of us seeks to juggle life's challenges.

I thought that if I could list the suggestions that I found helped me in this situation as an unpaid carer then these "tips" could be passed on to you and others like you, to help make your experience less traumatic, less stressful and much more positive both for you and for your loved-one!

FEEL THE LOVE
111 Tips
Volume 2
When Caring For Someone at Home



EBook : ISBN 978-0-9933513-1-0
Paperback: ISBN 978-0-9933513-3-4